DEEP SPACE

DEEP SPACE

NEW PICTURES FROM THE HUBBLE SPACE TELESCOPE

SIMON GOODWIN
& JOHN GRIBBIN

With a foreword by
DR PAUL ROCHE
Education Manager,
National Space Science Centre

CONSTABLE · LONDON

First published in Great Britain 1999 by Constable and Company Limited
3 The Lanchesters, 162 Fulham Palace Road, London W6 9ER

ISBN 0 09 479670 X
Printed in Hong Kong through World Print Ltd

A CIP catalogue record for this book is available from the British Library

CONTENTS

ACKNOWLEDGEMENTS

Thanks go to Ian King at CPL for help with image processing, to the Space Telescope Science Institute and to Dr Paul Roche.

AUTHOR'S NOTE

This book follows the standard scientific practice in using the (American) billion of a thousand million (1 000 000 000), not the (British) billion of a million million (1 000 000 000 000).

Distances across the Solar System are usually given by astronomers in terms of the average distance between the Earth and the Sun, which is defined as one astronomical unit (1 AU). In round numbers, 1 AU = 150 million kilometres (about 93 million miles). Since light takes 499 seconds to cover this distance, this distance can also be referred to as 499 light seconds, or 8.3 light minutes.

FOREWORD

Yet another coffee-table book full of the latest digitally enhanced images from the Hubble Space Telescope? Yet more fantastically coloured, mystery-laden pictures to baffle and bemuse the public? So often the role of imagery in astronomy is, at least in the public perception, merely to generate scenes of distant places where masses, sizes, distances and forces are all on such unimaginable scales that the layperson can only appreciate the aesthetic beauty and wonder at the genius required to interpret and understand them. But here we have something more than just a glossy collection of imagery, as Simon Goodwin and John Gribbin extend their reach beyond the Solar System and their previous collaboration, *Empire of the Sun*, to explore and explain the mysteries of *Deep Space*. As with Simon Goodwin's *Hubble's Universe*, they have carefully chosen the very best of the recent Hubble Space Telescope (HST) images, and prepared an explanatory text which reveals the secrets of these pictures to the public. You will find gathered here some of the most significant images of our Universe yet obtained, and insights into how they are used by astronomers to address some of the fundamental questions of astronomy and cosmology. Within these pages are gathered scenes of the birth, life and (often spectacular) death of planets, stars, galaxies and quasars, and glimpses of the large-scale structure of the Universe. These pictures show some of our best images of protoplanetary disks, and our first views of the optical counterparts to the enigmatic gamma-ray bursts (now known to lie at enormous distances). Data extracted from some of the images are being used to determine the elusive Hubble constant, and thus put an age on our Universe.

The HST was the first and most eagerly awaited of NASA's so-called Great Observatories, subsequently followed by the Compton Gamma Ray Observatory (GRO) and shortly to be joined by the Chandra X-ray Observatory (CXO, formerly known as AXAF) and finally the Space Infrared Telescope Facility (SIRTF). The public perception that the HST was somehow a costly 'failure', hamstrung by its imperfect mirror which effectively rendered it short-sighted until the COSTAR corrective optics were fitted in 1993, has given way to an appreciation of the advances that have rapidly flowed from the images it has gathered, whether ultraviolet, optical or infrared. In professional quarters, there is an acceptance that the HST can generate the sort of international interest that cannot be excited by a radio map, an X-ray image or a gamma-ray spectrum, no matter how significant they are in their respective fields. NASA has been keen to emphasize the ground-breaking work that the HST has made possible, and the easy and rapid distribution of information via the Internet has led to a surge in the educational usage of 'real' data. It is now possible to 'see' the Hubble Deep Field (Plate 37) in Braille, to estimate the Hubble constant and hence the age of the Universe, to measure relativistic quasar jet velocities, all using educational materials provided by the Space Telescope Science Institute (STScl) at its Website. Never before has there been such easy access to such visually stunning and scientifically exciting data for the non-specialist. Books such as this one play a vital role in emphasizing that you don't need a Ph.D. in astrophysics to learn something about the Universe, provided you are suitably guided along the way.

It is perhaps unfortunate for those who work in less visual disciplines (pun intended) such as radio, X-ray and gamma-ray astronomy, that the HST grabs so much of the limelight, but even a cursory examination of the following pages will show that this is entirely justified. The startling clarity of the images is still better than the best that even the mightiest of ground-based mirrors such as the twin 10-metre giants of the W. M. Keck Observatory on Mauna Kea, Hawaii, can manage, no matter what technological wizardry is applied to their optical systems. In a few years' time the HST will doubtless be superseded in the infrared and possibly the optical region by the rapid improvements in mirror design, active and adaptive optics, CCD design and other technologies that are being pioneered at several sites, but in the ultraviolet it will continue to reign supreme for a while yet. But even now, plans are being developed for bigger and better space-based telescopes, and the Next Generation Space Telescope (NGST) promises to take astronomy to a whole new level of imaging capabilities. Waiting in the wings is Roger Angel, who has already moved mirror technology onwards in a series of previously undreamed of leaps. There is no telling where we will be a decade from now, when the HST has been 'ungracefully retired' from active service – it's hard to gracefully retire ten tonnes of metal, orbiting hundreds of kilometres above the surface, so a spectacular, incandescent re-entry is on the cards. There are rumours of plans afoot to retrieve the HST for use as an exhibit – a hugely costly option, but what a draw for a museum! The fact that such rumours are circulating is perhaps an indication of the esteem with which the HST is held among the astronomy and space community.

From the crude rock carvings recently identified as a 5 000-year-old Moon map at Knowth in Ireland, to these hot-off-the-presses (or more correctly, hot from the satellite downlink) HST pictures, astronomical images have always held a fascination. For many astronomers, it was the attraction of pictures of the planets, stars or galaxies that marked the starting point of their careers. For most professional astronomers it is actually rather unusual to work with images of the type shown here. There are so many sub-disciplines and specialities that they are more likely to spend their years measuring apparently unexciting (but information-packed) spectra, or counting incredibly rare (but energy-packed) gamma-ray photons, rather than unravelling the mysteries of the Universe from a single CCD frame. But the whole of astronomy, across the entire electromagnetic spectrum, and from our current Solar System outwards and back to the Big Bang, benefits from the great interest that the HST generates in the mass media.

From an educational perspective, there is no better way to fire up the imagination of a future generation of scientists than by letting them participate at the cutting edge of modern astronomy. Through the Internet, and the educational offices of NASA, HST data and resources have been distributed to schools and universities all over the world. Many developing countries are now beginning to increase their involvement in astronomical research, identifying it as a means of inspiring interest in science and technology and hoping that this will have the knock-on effect of improving levels of technological understanding. In the UK, we shall soon have a major science centre dedicated to the study of the Universe through ground- and space-based astronomy, the Millennium Commission funded National Space Science Centre at Leicester. It is perhaps significant that one of the fourteen Landmark Projects funded by the National Lottery programme is entirely a space-related venture, and I for one am hoping that this will spark a resurgence of interest in astronomy and space sciences. The generation that watched as men stepped onto the surface of the Moon for the first time is giving way to one which may see a man or woman walk on the surface of Mars. And who knows, maybe that person will have been inspired in their career choice by a book like *Deep Space*.

Dr Paul Roche
Director of Education
National Space Science Centre
Leicester

THE PICTURES

PLATE 1

LAUNCH OF *DISCOVERY*

February 1997 saw the launch of the Space Shuttle *Discovery* on the first Hubble Space Telescope (HST) routine servicing mission. The HST had been launched by this same Space Shuttle in April 1990 and placed in a low Earth orbit, 600 km above us, circling the Earth once every 97 minutes.

The HST represented a revolution in satellite design. It was the first to be constructed in such a way that repairs and servicing could be carried out in orbit. Its on-board instruments were easily replaceable, new ones simply being slotted into place by astronauts. This new design feature was to prove its worth when, shortly after launch, it was discovered that the main mirror was faulty.

The first images from the HST were disappointing – they were simply not of the quality that the HST's planners had hoped for. The 2.4-metre diameter mirror, it turned out, had not been ground to the correct specifications. The problem was solved in December 1993 when the crew of the Space Shuttle *Endeavour* repaired the telescope in an 11-day mission, installing new optics which compensated for the flaws in the mirror. The mission was hailed as a triumph for NASA and the Hubble Space Telescope, and its success did much to help retain funding for the Shuttle programme, which the US government was then considering cutting back.

PLATE 2

THE HUBBLE SPACE TELESCOPE IN ORBIT

The Hubble Space Telescope is roughly the size of a single-decker bus, 13.1 metres long and 4.3 metres in diameter at its widest point. At 11.6 tonnes it is a fairly hefty satellite, and it required the largest Space Shuttle, *Discovery*, to lift it into orbit. This picture shows the HST in *Discovery*'s cargo bay, held in place by the manipulator arm of the shuttle. While it is in the cargo bay, astronauts are able to move out to the telescope and repair and replace its different modules.

During this servicing mission two of the old instruments were replaced by new ones. Normal satellites have their technology 'frozen' a few years before launch when the design is finalized, but the HST is able to take advantage of developments in technology after its launch. Two new instruments were installed – the Near-Infrared Camera and Multi-Object Spectrometer (NICMOS) and the Space Telescope Imaging Spectrograph (STIS). These replaced the Faint Object Camera (FOC) and the Goddard High Resolution Spectrograph (GHRS). But the improved technology means that STIS actually does both jobs previously carried out by FOC and GHRS, so NICMOS represents an addition to the HST's capability.

More servicing missions are planned for the future, upgrading the telescope until the proposed end of its useful life a few years into the new millennium.

See glossary entries: NICMOS; STIS

PLATE 3

CLOSE-UP OF THE ORION NEBULA, M42

One of the most striking constellations in the sky is Orion, the mythical hunter. Four bright stars in a rectangle mark his shoulders and feet and frame the three stars of his belt. Just below the belt is a fuzzy patch of light just visible to the naked eye. This is part of a huge cloud of gas and dust known as the Orion Nebula, from which stars are being born. At a distance of 1500 light years, it is one of the closest star-forming regions to us, and it is in a region such as this that our own Sun was probably born.

The Orion Nebula began to make stars a mere 300 000 years ago (on astronomical timescales this is equivalent to yesterday). The newly born stars cause the gas around them to glow as they heat it up and blow it away. The plume of material in the upper left of the picture is hot gas that has been blown out of a particularly large star just outside the picture.

This picture shows a small part of the Orion Nebula. The entire neighbourhood, made up mostly of the cool, hydrogen-containing clouds known as HI regions, was examined in detail using the Wide Field and Planetary Camera 2 (WF/PC-2), an imaging instrument placed on the Hubble Space Telescope during the 1993 repair mission.

See glossary entries: HI region; nebula; Sun; WF/PC

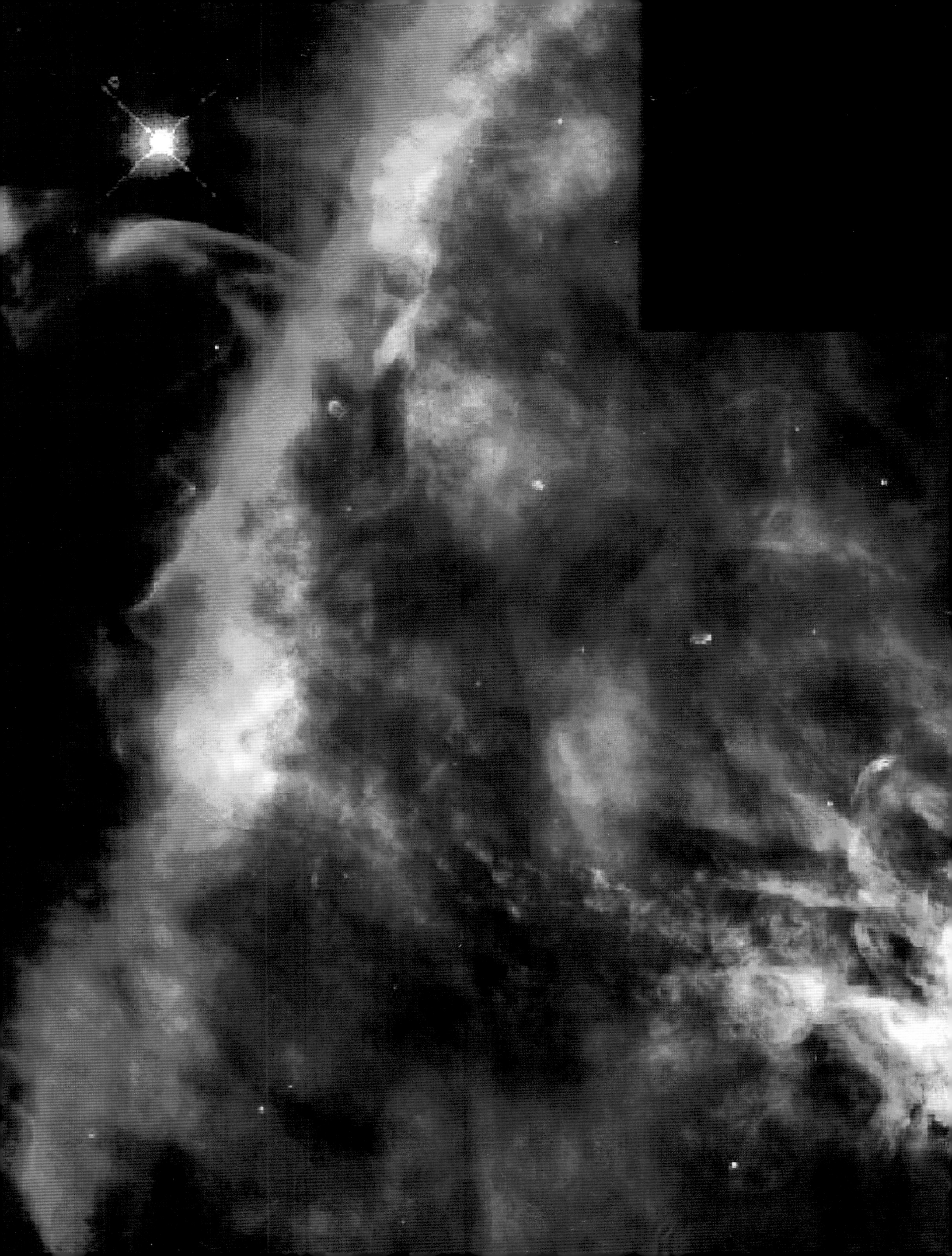

PLATE 4

OMC-1: INSIDE THE ORION MOLECULAR CLOUD

Hidden within the Orion Nebula are regions of intense star formation. Stars form when clouds of gas become unstable as gravity pulls parts of the clouds down onto themselves. These clumps of gas get denser and hotter as they collapse. Eventually the temperature and pressure at the centres of these so-called protostars are so great that they trigger nuclear fusion. This happens when hydrogen atoms (strictly speaking, hydrogen nuclei, the cores of the atoms) hit one another fast enough and often enough to stick together. The upshot is that four hydrogen atoms turn themselves into one helium atom. Huge amounts of energy are released in the process, and the star starts to shine.

When young, the stars are still shrouded in gas and dust from their parent cloud, and are invisible in normal light. The Hubble Space Telescope does not just look in normal ('visible') light, however. It is also able to image in infrared light (light with wavelengths a little longer than those of visible light) and ultraviolet light (light with wavelengths a little shorter than those of visible light). This picture was taken in infrared light by the Near-Infrared Camera and Multi-Object Spectrometer (NICMOS), which can see through the dense clouds of gas and dust around these stars.

OMC-1 is a denser region of gas, known as a molecular core, within the gas cloud known as the Orion Molecular Cloud (OMC). The cloud gets its name for the obvious reason that it is largely made of gas (chiefly hydrogen) in the form of molecules, not as individual atoms. In many places within OMC-1, gravity has compressed the gas to the point where stars are forming at the moment.

This image is of a region only 0.4 light years across, and shows features as small as our own Solar System. The big, bright star at the centre of the picture is throwing off gas at high speeds at its poles, producing the two lines of hot material coming off the star at 11 o'clock and 5 o'clock.

See glossary entries: infrared light; light year; molecular cloud; NICMOS

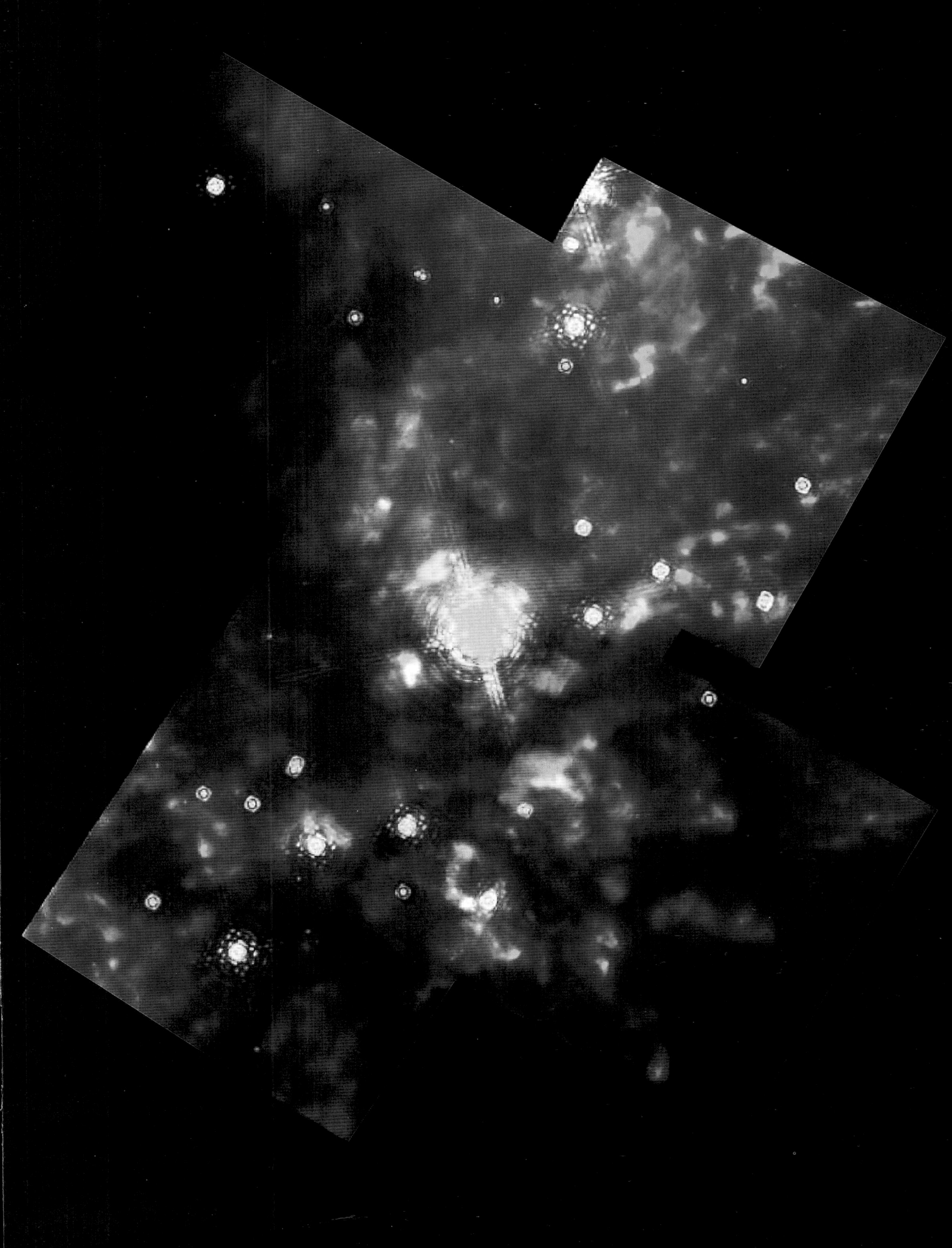

PLATE 5

THE LAGOON NEBULA, M8

The Lagoon Nebula is another region in which stars are being born. The nebula contains a central bright star called Herschel 36 which is several times bigger than the Sun and a lot brighter.

The bigger a star is, the faster it burns its nuclear fuel. This means that huge stars like Herschel 36 do not live for very long – tens of millions of years rather than the 10 billion years we expect for the Sun – but they live faster. And because they produce energy at a much higher rate, large stars are much brighter than stars like the Sun. Wherever we see massive stars we therefore know that star formation is going on, or has occurred recently (in astronomical terms). They are so bright that they act as announcers of star formation, showing us where to look for young stars of all masses.

Herschel 36 is heating the gas around it, blowing away some gas and causing other gas to glow brightly. In this image much of the complex structure of the gas cloud can be seen. Dense, cold gas that has not yet been heated by massive stars (another HI region) partly obscures the view of Herschel 36.

See glossary entries: HI region; nebula; Sun

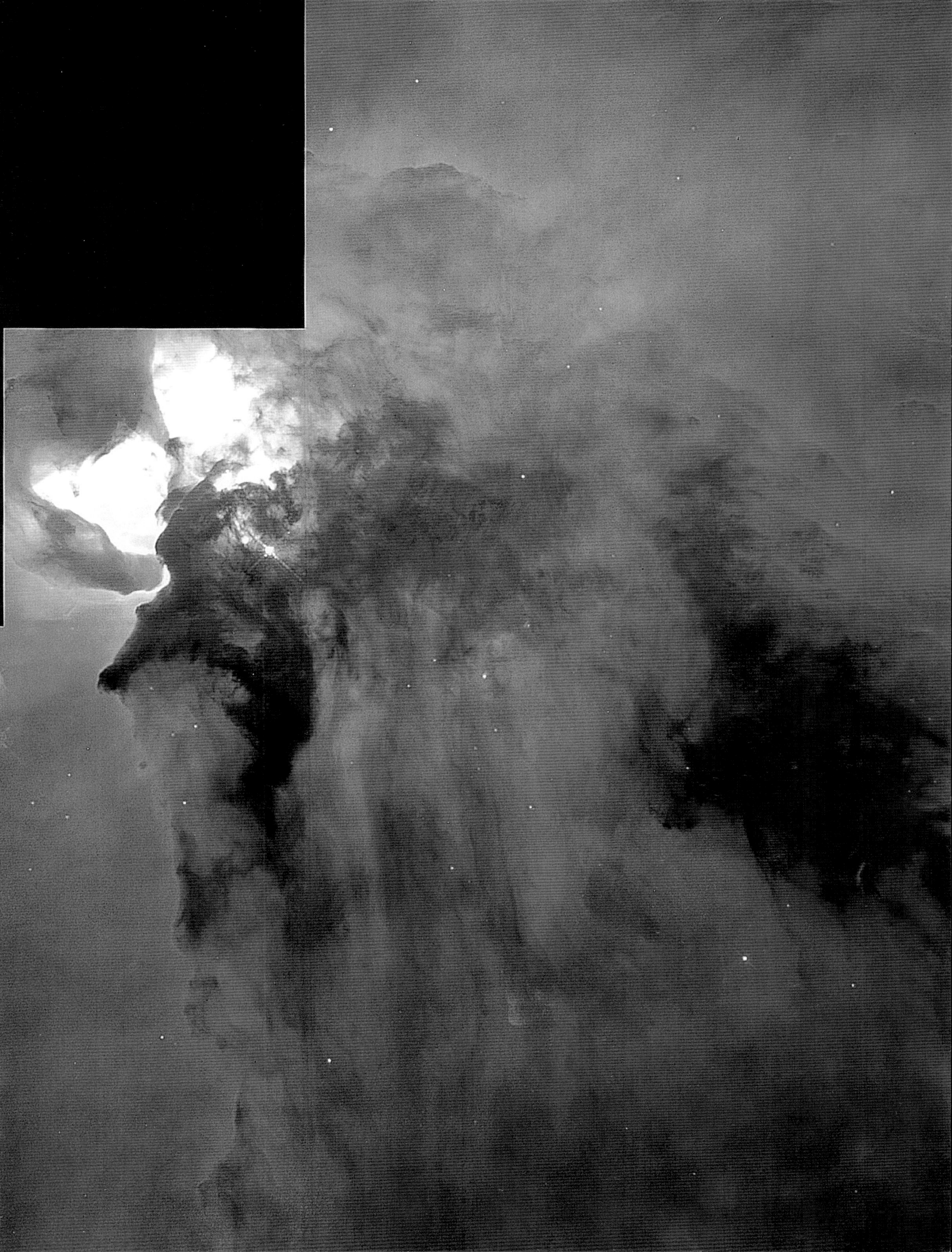

PLATE 6

THE STAR HERSCHEL 36

This close-up of the centre of the Lagoon Nebula shows Herschel 36 surrounded by 'twisters' of cold gas. These tornado-like structures are probably formed by the intense radiation from the massive star. Temperature differences between the heated surfaces and the cold interiors of the clouds produce a twisting force which wraps the clouds around themselves.

Colourful interstellar clouds like this may look familiar to anyone who has seen the Star Trek movie *Insurrection*. The special effects in the movie were based on Hubble images, but the colours are not true to life. These images are given 'false colour' to enhance the detail – to our eyes, the clouds would actually look a dull grey-brown if we could get close enough to see them.

This image was taken using the WF/PC-2. The wide-field camera shows a large area of the sky, while the planetary camera shows a more detailed image of a smaller area. (It is so named because one of its jobs is to image planets within our own Solar System in detail.) Since the field of view of the planetary camera is smaller, many images taken by WF/PC-2 have a 'staircase' shape, with a corner missing.

See glossary entry: WF/PC

PLATE 7

A MASSIVE STAR AND FAMILY IN NGC 2264

This picture shows a huge young star in the cluster NGC 2264, known as NGC 2264 IRS. Hidden behind a cloud of dust and gas, this star can be seen only in the infrared; again, this is a NICMOS image.

Around NGC 2264 IRS are six baby Sun-like stars. These stars are all very close together, well within one-tenth of a light year. The smaller stars were formed when radiation and material flowed away from the massive star at high speed and compressed the surrounding gas. This compression gave gravity a head start, causing some regions to collapse and form smaller stars.

The spikes emanating from NGC 2264 IRS are not real. They are caused by light being diffracted by some of the struts which support part of the optics of the Hubble Space Telescope itself – rather like water waves bending around an obstruction. Because the astronomers know exactly where these struts are, and how big they are, they can calculate exactly what kind of diffraction spikes should be produced if the mirror is working perfectly; the pattern we see is very close to what a hypothetical 'perfect telescope' would produce.

See glossary entries: infrared light; light year; NICMOS; Sun

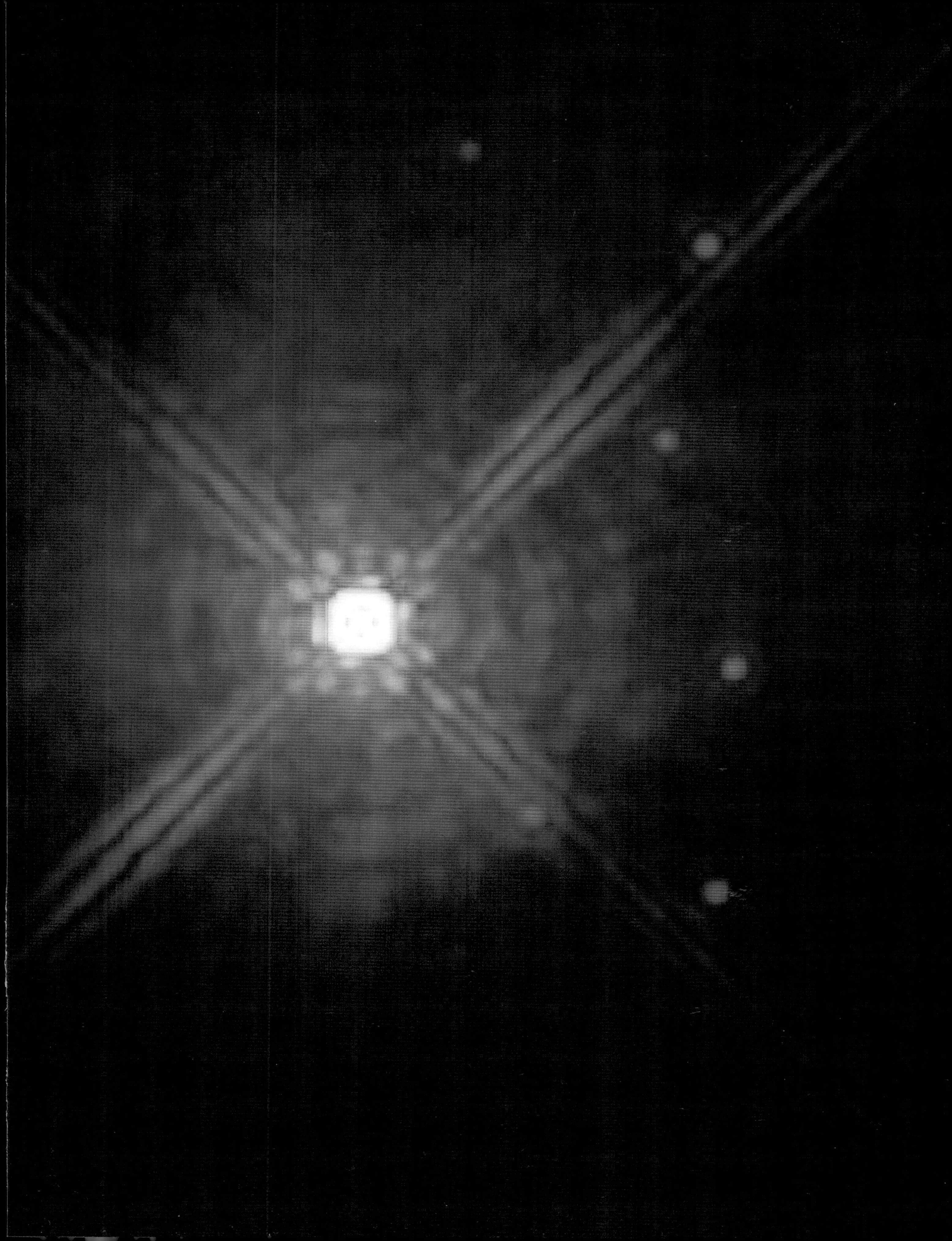

PLATE 8

A BRIGHT STAR-FORMING REGION, NGC 2363

In this nebula, which lies 10 million light years away, two large clusters of stars can be seen lying close together. At the top of the picture and relatively free of gas is a group of stars about 4 or 5 million years old. The gas from which these stars were formed (a hot, hydrogen-containing cloud known as an HII region) has been blown away, and its shell can be seen around the cluster. Below this cluster is a younger cluster, only 2 million years old, still embedded in the gas from which it formed.

NGC 2363 lies outside our own Milky Way galaxy in the galaxy NGC 2366. The Milky Way contains several hundred billion stars and is about 100 000 light years across. The distances between galaxies are measured in millions of light years.

The brightest star in this picture, to the right of the upper cluster, is a very rare type of star known as a luminous blue variable. These are very massive stars, 30 to 60 times the mass of the Sun, whose size makes them very unstable. These stars throw off their outer layers from time to time, causing their brightness to change considerably.

See glossary entries: HII region; light year; Milky Way; nebula

PLATE 9

A GIANT STAR-FORMING REGION IN M33

This giant star-forming nebula, designated NGC 604, is an incredible 1500 light years across and contains around 200 very massive stars. In comparison, the Orion Nebula contains only four massive stars and is only a few tens of light years across.

These massive stars have blown a hole in the gas cloud from which they were formed, allowing us to see down inside the cloud to where the young cluster of stars sits. The gas around these massive stars, forming an HII region, is at 10 000 K (kelvin), heated by the radiation pouring from the hot stars.

NGC 604 is 2.7 million light years away, in the neighbouring galaxy M33. This is a spiral galaxy, similar to the Milky Way, in the constellation Triangulum.

See glossary entries: HII region; kelvin; light year; nebula; spiral galaxy

PLATE 10

YOUNG STAR CLUSTER

Another brightly glowing star-forming cloud, called N81, is shown in this picture. The Hubble Space Telescope allows us to see that there are actually 50 stars in the centre of this cloud (not all visible on this large-scale image). All these stars lie within 10 light years of one another, a very tightly packed region of space – around the Sun there are only a handful of stars within that distance.

Dark patches of dusty gas cross the centre of the nebula, obscuring some of the interior. Eventually these lanes of dust will be heated up and blown away.

N81 lies 200 000 light years away in a small satellite galaxy of the Milky Way known as the Small Magellanic Cloud (SMC). The SMC is orbiting our Galaxy, and the gravitational interactions between the two galaxies is disturbing the gas in the SMC, stimulating star formation there.

See glossary entry: light year

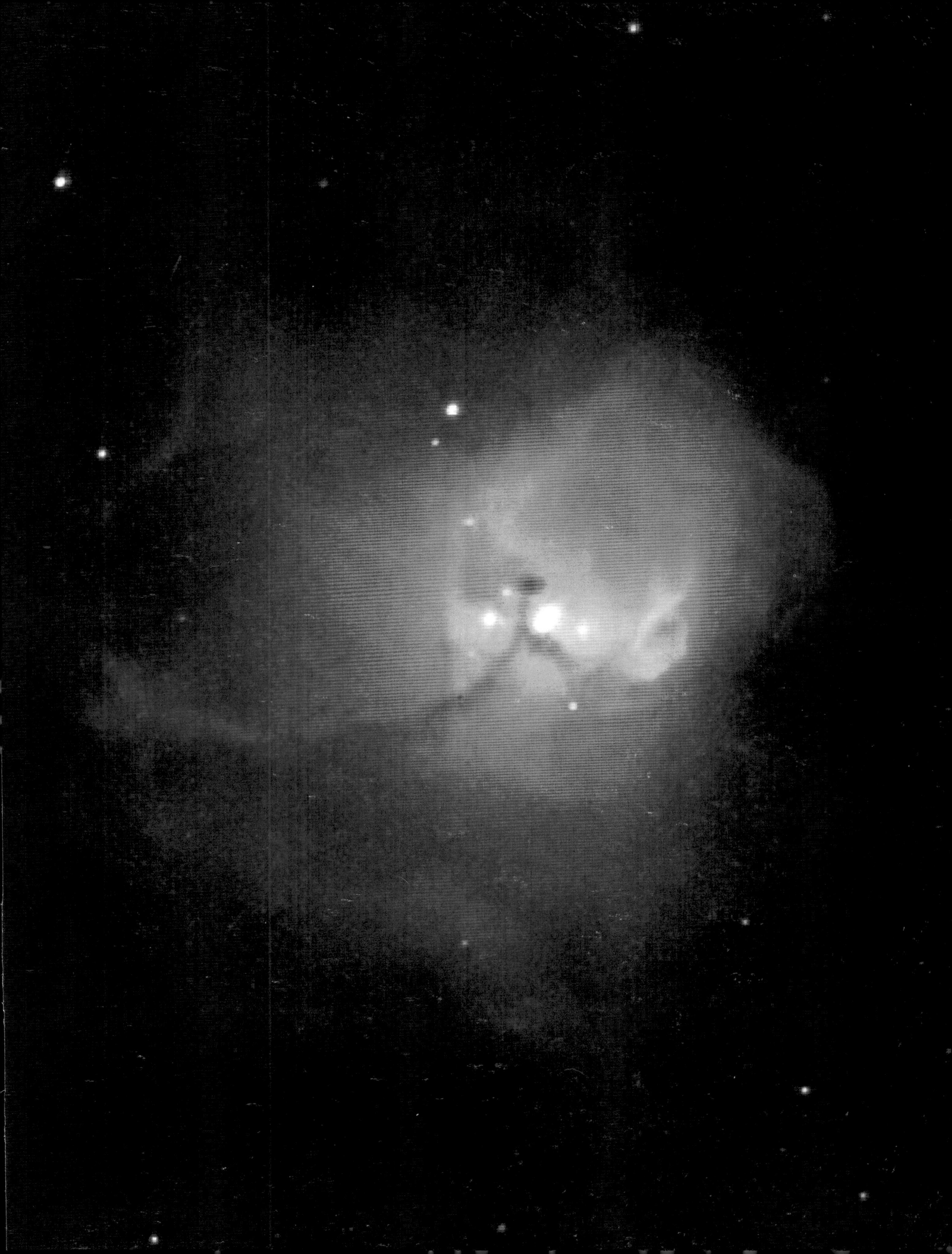

PLATE 11

THE MASSIVE STAR CLUSTER NGC 1818

The cluster of stars known as NGC 1818 was formed about 40 million years ago. It has blown away the remains of the gas cloud from which it formed, and now lies open to our gaze.

The Hubble Space Telescope was able to see more than 20 000 individual stars in this cluster. Most of them are smaller than the Sun, but a few very bright, massive stars can be seen. Circled is a tiny, hot white dwarf star.

This white dwarf, which has a surface temperature of about 2500 K, was a star about 7.5 times as massive as the Sun, and is in its twilight years. Previously, astronomers thought that stars between about 6 and 10 times the mass of the Sun would blow themselves completely apart after a few tens of millions of years, but this discovery has shown that they can end in a similar way to smaller stars, including the Sun.

See glossary entries: kelvin; white dwarf

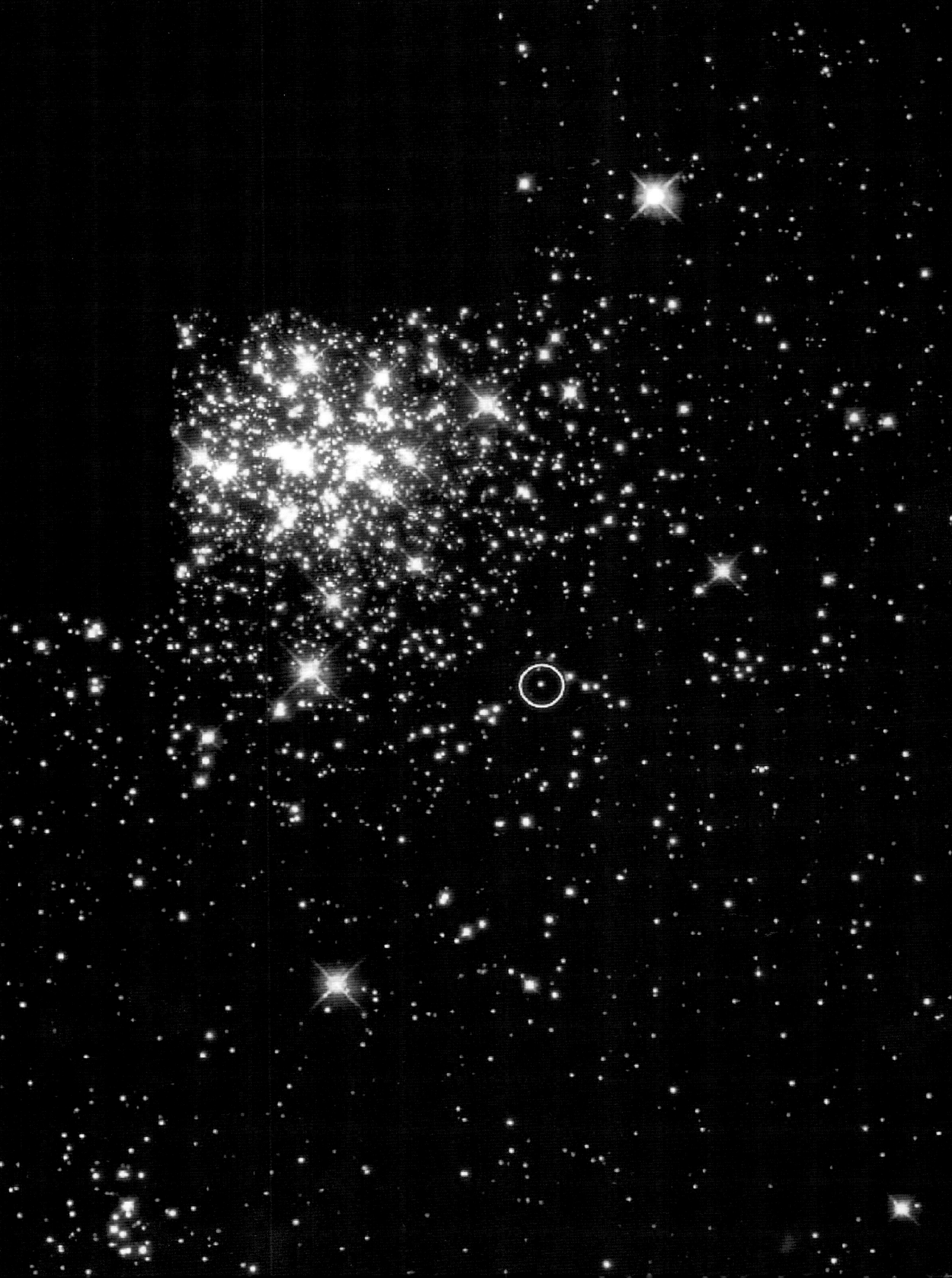

PLATE 12

GLOBULAR CLUSTER GC1 IN ANDROMEDA

Some of the oldest objects in the Universe are clusters of stars like this one, known as globular clusters from their spherical appearance. Most globular clusters formed during the very earliest stages of galaxy formation, and the oldest are estimated to be about 12 billion years old.

This globular cluster, known as GC1 or Mayall II, is in orbit around our closest major galactic neighbour, the Andromeda Galaxy (M31). Since they are so old, globular clusters are 'fossils' from the early history of the Universe. In globular clusters, all stars larger than about the size of the Sun have evolved and died, leaving the clusters full of small, red stars. Before the Hubble Space Telescope was launched, globular clusters at the distance of GC1 (about 3 million light years) or farther were too small to be seen as anything other than points of light. Now, however, we can study the structure of these fossils around some of our closer galactic neighbours.

The two bright objects to the top left and centre right of GC1 are stars in our own Galaxy that just happen to lie in the same direction as GC1. They appear so much brighter than the stars in GC1 because they are so much closer (probably only a few hundred or a thousand light years away at most).

See glossary entries: globular cluster; light year

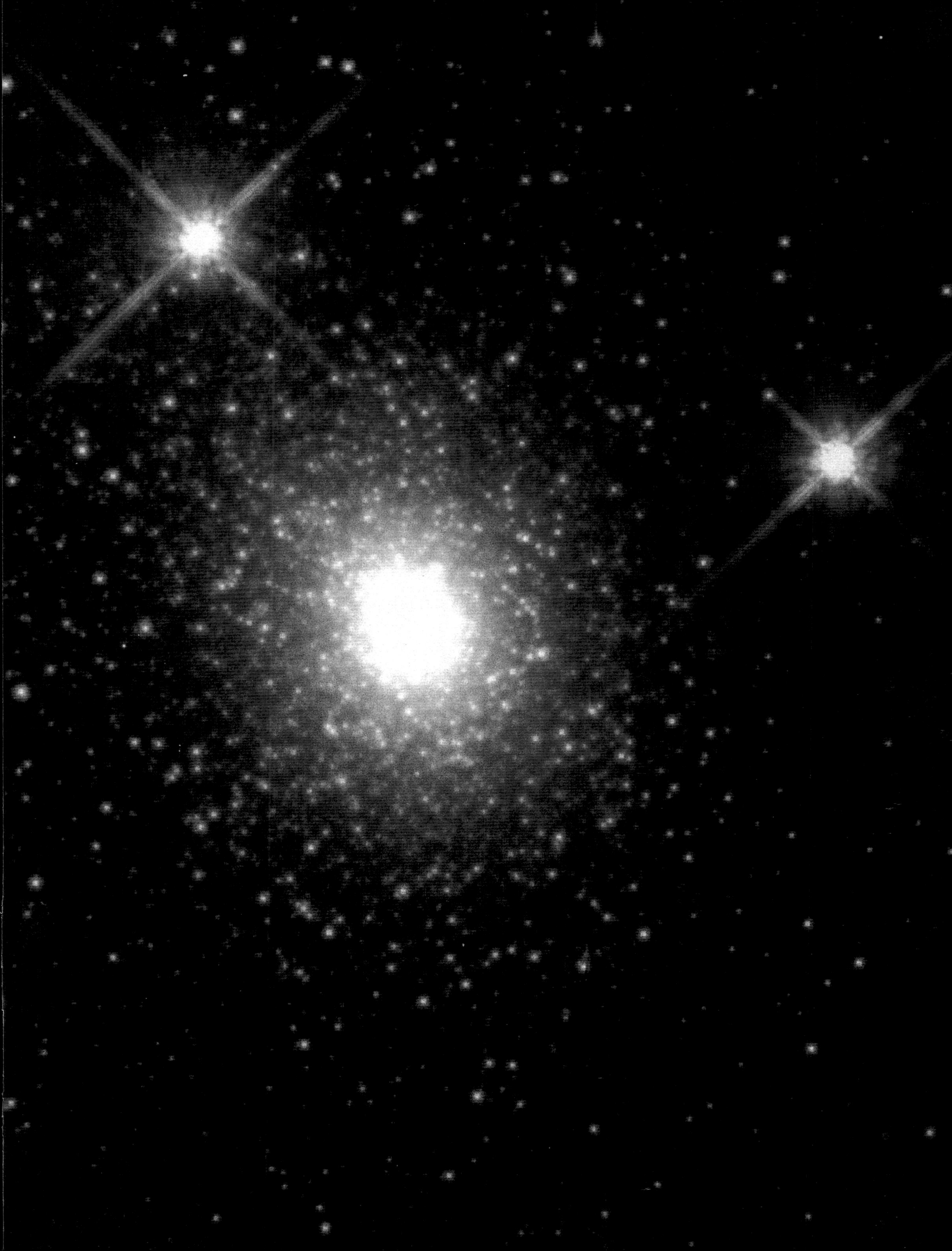

PLATE 13

IMAGING BETELGEUSE

At first glance this picture is not very impressive; but it is a testimony to the amazing power of the Hubble Space Telescope. This is the first image of a star other than our Sun to show anything more than a point of light. Betelgeuse is a huge giant star nearing the end of its life. Having exhausted its supplies of hydrogen to 'burn' into helium, this star has swollen up and begun to burn helium into carbon in its core to release energy (add three helium atoms together in just the right way and you get a carbon atom). Betelgeuse is 800 times the diameter of the Sun.

Even though Betelgeuse is so large, its great distance means that previously it has appeared just as a point of light, as do all the other stars. But the HST can see very fine detail – this picture is equivalent to photographing a car headlight from nearly 10 000 km away! Not only was the HST able to resolve the surface of the star, but it showed a strange hot spot on the star's surface (just below the centre of the image) which is around 2000 K hotter than the rest of the star. The origin of the spot is unclear. It may be related to strong magnetic fields from deep inside Betelgeuse, or possibly to oscillations in the star.

See glossary entries: kelvin; red giant; Sun

PLATE 14

SEPARATING MIRA A AND B

Like the image of Betelgeuse, this picture is not the most visually stunning we have to show, but it helps to illustrate the power of the HST. Pictured here for the first time are the two stars of the Mira binary system, 250 light years away from us. The distance between these stars is 40 times the distance between the Earth and the Sun, and they take 14 years to orbit each other. As it appears to us, this separation is equivalent to the length of a grain of rice seen from 4 km away.

The smaller of the two stars (Mira B, rather obviously) is slightly non-spherical. The gravitational pull of Mira A, which is a red giant like Betelgeuse, may be pulling the smaller star out of shape. Tidal forces are also stripping material from the larger star and dumping it onto the smaller one.

This image has a rather 'blocky' appearance because it represents the HST's extreme limit of resolution. Each block is a single pixel (picture element) of the electronic imaging system (CCD) of the telescope.

See glossary entries: binary system; charge coupled device (CCD); light year; red giant

PLATE 15

WR124: A VIOLENT WOLF–RAYET STAR

At the other end of the scale from rather dull stars like the Sun, Betelgeuse, or Mira A and B, are stars such as WR124, shown in this WF/PC-2 image. WR124 is in the process of blowing itself apart.

WR124 is a Wolf–Rayet star, a very rare supermassive class of star with about 60 times the Sun's mass and surface temperatures of up to 50 000 K. The nebula of material around WR124 was ejected from the star about 10 000 years ago and is expanding into space at 150 000 km/h. This expansion is not smooth, and the material tends to clump together, each clump being a few tens of times heavier than the Earth.

Wolf–Rayet stars are probably massive stars near the end of their lives. WR124 will not live very long. It is burning its nuclear fuel at such a prodigious rate that it will be exhausted in only a few million years. What ultimately happens to very massive stars is still unclear. The evolutionary paths of stars like the Sun are reasonably well understood, but the speed at which massive stars burn their various nuclear fuels makes it difficult to plot the course of their evolution.

See glossary entries: kelvin; Sun; WF/PC

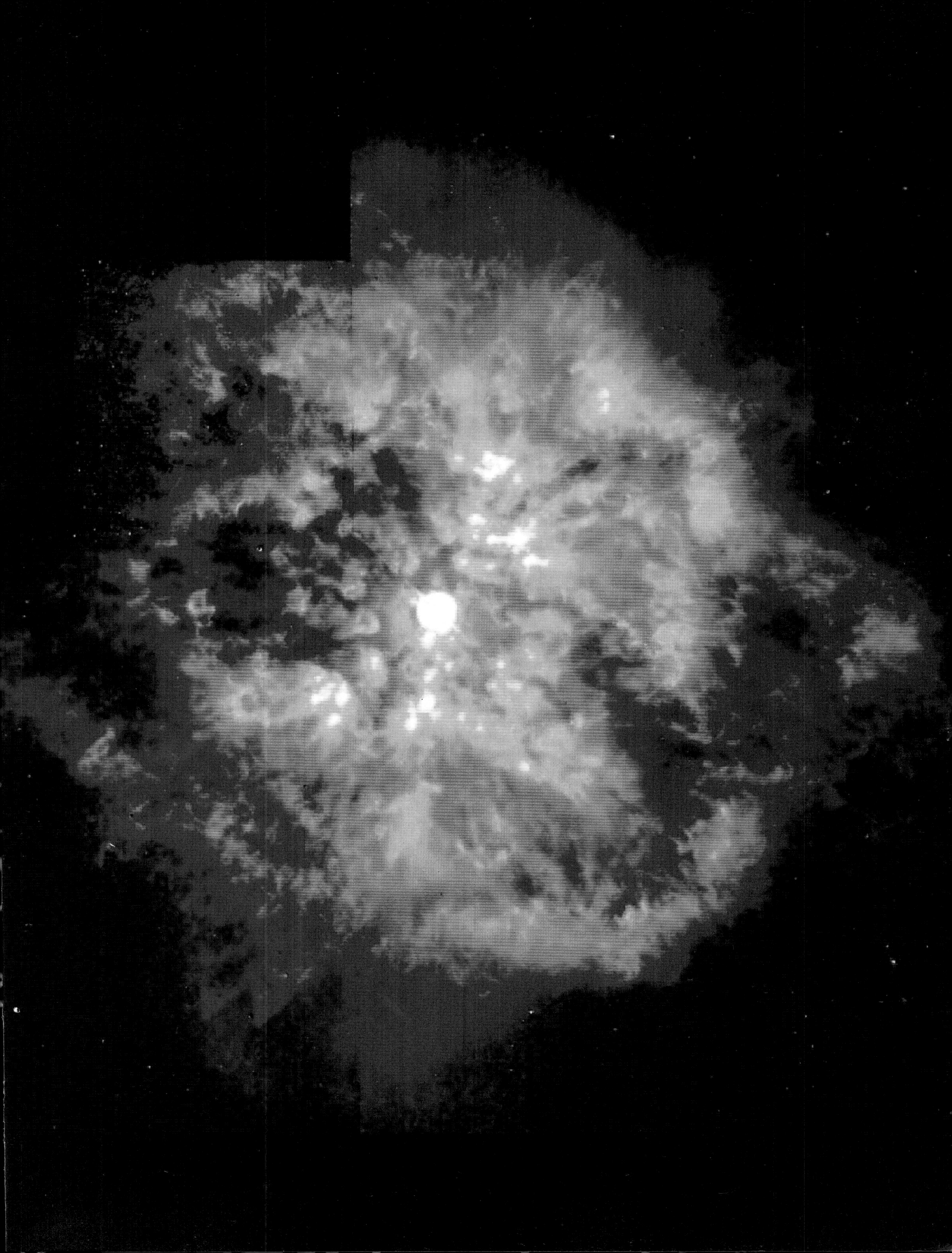

PLATE 16

THE PISTOL STAR: THE BRIGHTEST STAR?

Even more impressive than WR124 is the Pistol Star, discovered in the early 1990s. Even though it lies 25 000 light years away in the constellation Sagittarius, this star can still be seen with the naked eye, shining with the light of 10 million Suns. It is probably around 100 times as massive as the Sun, although when it was born it may have had twice that mass.

In a star like the Sun, the inward pull of gravity is exactly countered by the outward push of radiation created in the heart of the star. This is why the Sun is so stable (happily for us). In stars as big as the Pistol Star, the outward push of radiation can often overcome gravity; every few thousand years this star blows off material amounting to several times the Sun's mass.

Looking in the infrared, NICMOS was able to penetrate the dust and gas surrounding the Pistol Star to see the structure of the ejected material. The largest shell of material is now about 4 light years across, while the material that can be seen in this image was ejected in two bursts, about 6000 and 4000 years ago.

Stars this size are extremely rare. The vast majority of stars are the size of the Sun or smaller (the Sun is actually quite large by stellar standards).

See glossary entries: light year; Sun

PLATE 17

THE CENTRE OF THE CRAB NEBULA, M1

Stars like WR124 and the Pistol Star will end their lives in the most spectacular way – as supernova explosions. When all of a star's nuclear fuel is finally exhausted, there is no longer any energy being generated to hold the star up against the inward pull of gravity. In a tiny fraction of a second the core of the star collapses in on itself, and the outer layers are ejected at speeds of 7 million km/h.

The Crab Nebula is the remnant of a supernova that exploded 7000 light years away, and was visible from Earth over 900 years ago. As light travels at a finite (but very fast – 1 billion km/h) speed, when we look into the night sky we see things as they were in the past. So the supernova actually exploded in about 6000 BC, but the light from the explosion took 7000 years to reach us. It was seen and described by Chinese astronomers, who called it a 'guest star'.

At the centre of the nebula is a pulsar, the super-compact core of the star left behind after the supernova explosion. Gravity has crushed the equivalent of the mass of the Sun into a sphere around 10 km across. This compact object is spinning thirty times a second, and its intense magnetic field is sweeping up charged particles and beaming energy towards us, like some high-energy cosmic lighthouse.

See glossary entries: light year; look-back time; pulsar; supernova

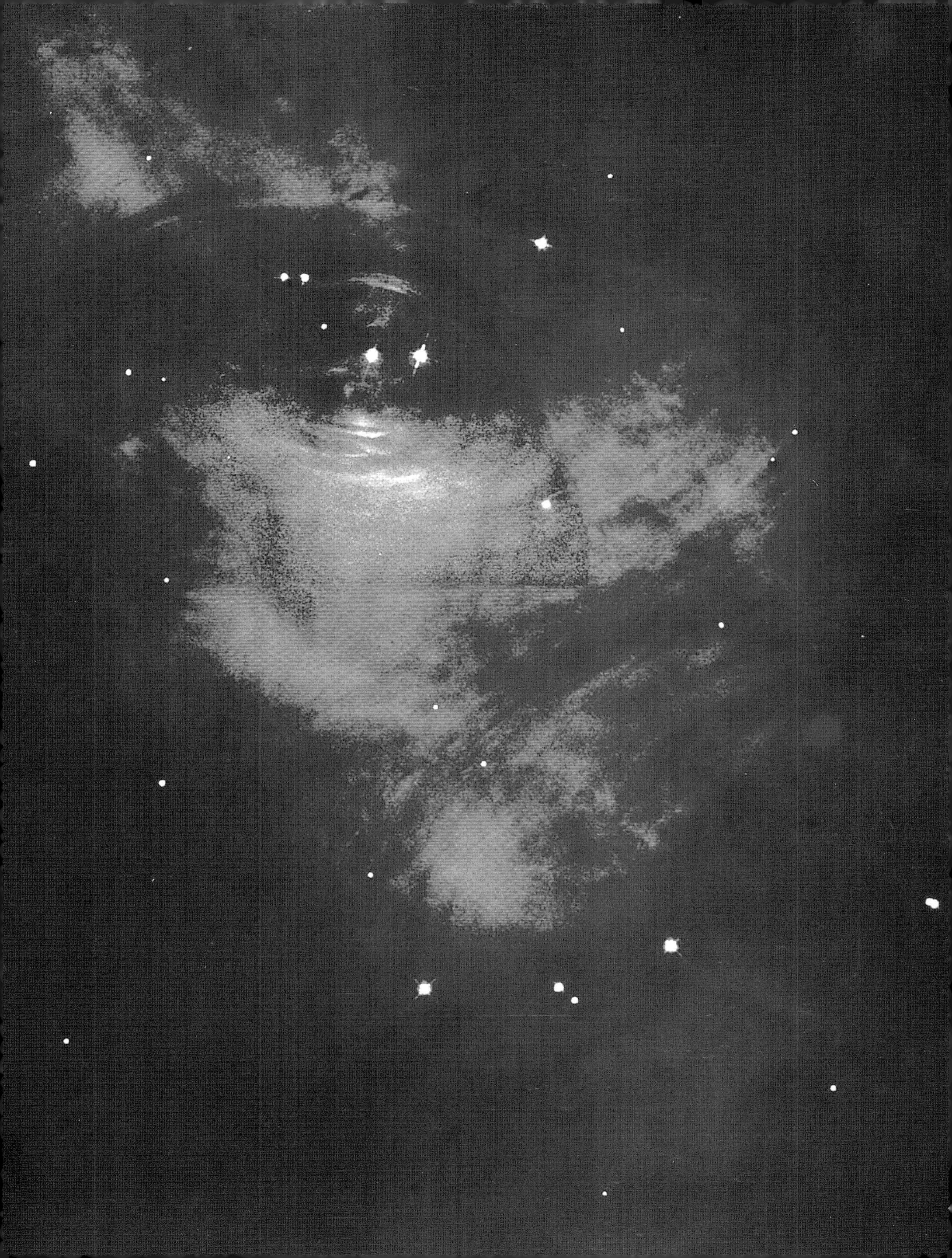

PLATE 18

SUPERNOVA 1987A IN THE LARGE MAGELLANIC CLOUD

Near the centre of this picture are the remains of a star that was seen from Earth as a supernova in February 1987. What made this supernova so special was that it was in one of the Milky Way's satellite galaxies, the Large Magellanic Cloud, and gave astronomers the best chance they have ever had to study a new supernova – a mere 150 000 light years away. (Most supernovae that are detected are in galaxies many millions of light years distant.) This supernova, designated SN 1987A, was so bright that it was visible with the naked eye – if you were lucky enough to be in the southern hemisphere.

After SN 1987A, astronomers were able to go back through the records to discover exactly which star had exploded. The star responsible turned out to be a massive star around 20 times heavier than the Sun and about 12 million years old. The region around the site of the supernova, shown here in this wide view, is packed with massive stars. The Large Magellanic Cloud is forming large numbers of stars at the moment. Many of the stars visible here will also end their lives in a supernova in the next few million years.

Supernova 1987A probably also left a pulsar, although one that is not sending its beam of radio waves directly towards us.

See glossary entries: light year; Milky Way; pulsar; supernova

PLATE 19

THE RING NEBULA, M57

A star like the Sun will quietly burn hydrogen in its core for billions or tens of billions of years. It is estimated that the Sun is 5 billion years old, and has enough hydrogen for another 5 billion years – long enough for its energy reserves not to give us cause for concern. Eventually, though, even the Sun will reach the end of its quiet life and expand to become a red giant similar to Betelgeuse (Plate 13). It is when even the helium in Sun-like stars is exhausted that things get interesting.

The outer layers of the star are thrown off to produce a planetary nebula, such as the Ring Nebula shown here. The colours tell us what type of atom is emitting the light: blue is helium (the hottest parts of the nebula), green is oxygen and red is nitrogen (the coolest parts of the nebula). The variation in the temperature of the nebula from the inside to the outside can thus be clearly seen. The nebula is actually a spherical shell around the central star. It looks like a ring because there we are looking through the edge of the sphere where there is more gas along our line of sight.

See glossary entry: planetary nebula

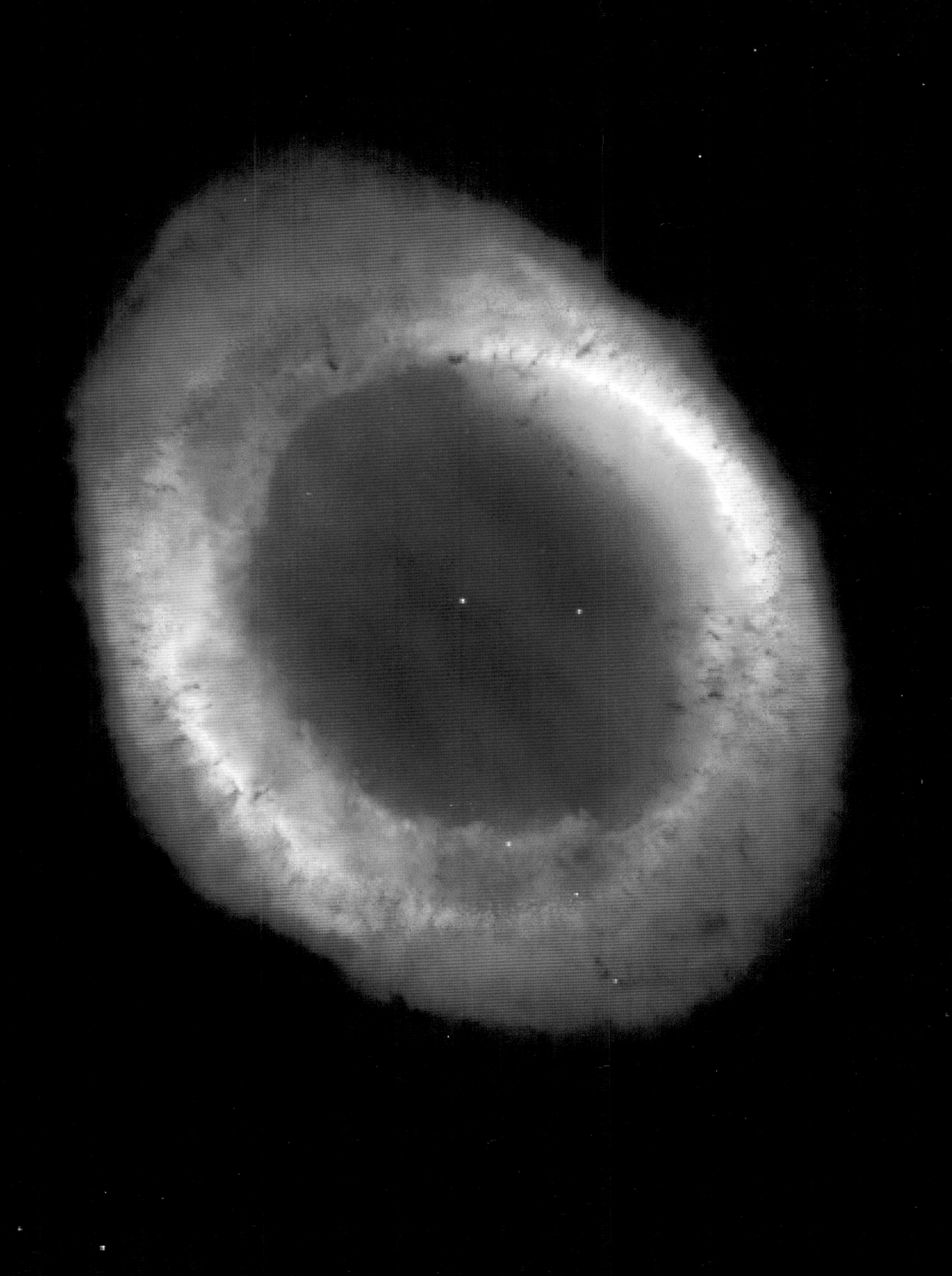

PLATE 20

PLANETARY NEBULA IC 3568

Planetary nebulae have nothing to do with planets. They are so called as many of them, like IC 3568 here, show a planet-like disk when viewed through a telescope. About 1500 planetary nebulae in our Galaxy have been catalogued, but it is estimated that at least ten times as many have still not been studied in detail. The visible nebula shines because it is absorbing ultraviolet radiation from the central star and getting hot; there is probably much more cool, dark gas farther out from the star which does not shine in this way.

IC 3568, 9000 light years away in the constellation Camelopardalis, is a prime example of a circular planetary nebula. The ejection of material from the central star of IC 3568 was smooth, and the diameter of the shell is now about 0.4 light years, about 600 times the diameter of the orbit of Neptune around the Sun in our own Solar System.

See glossary entries: light year; planetary nebula; ultraviolet light

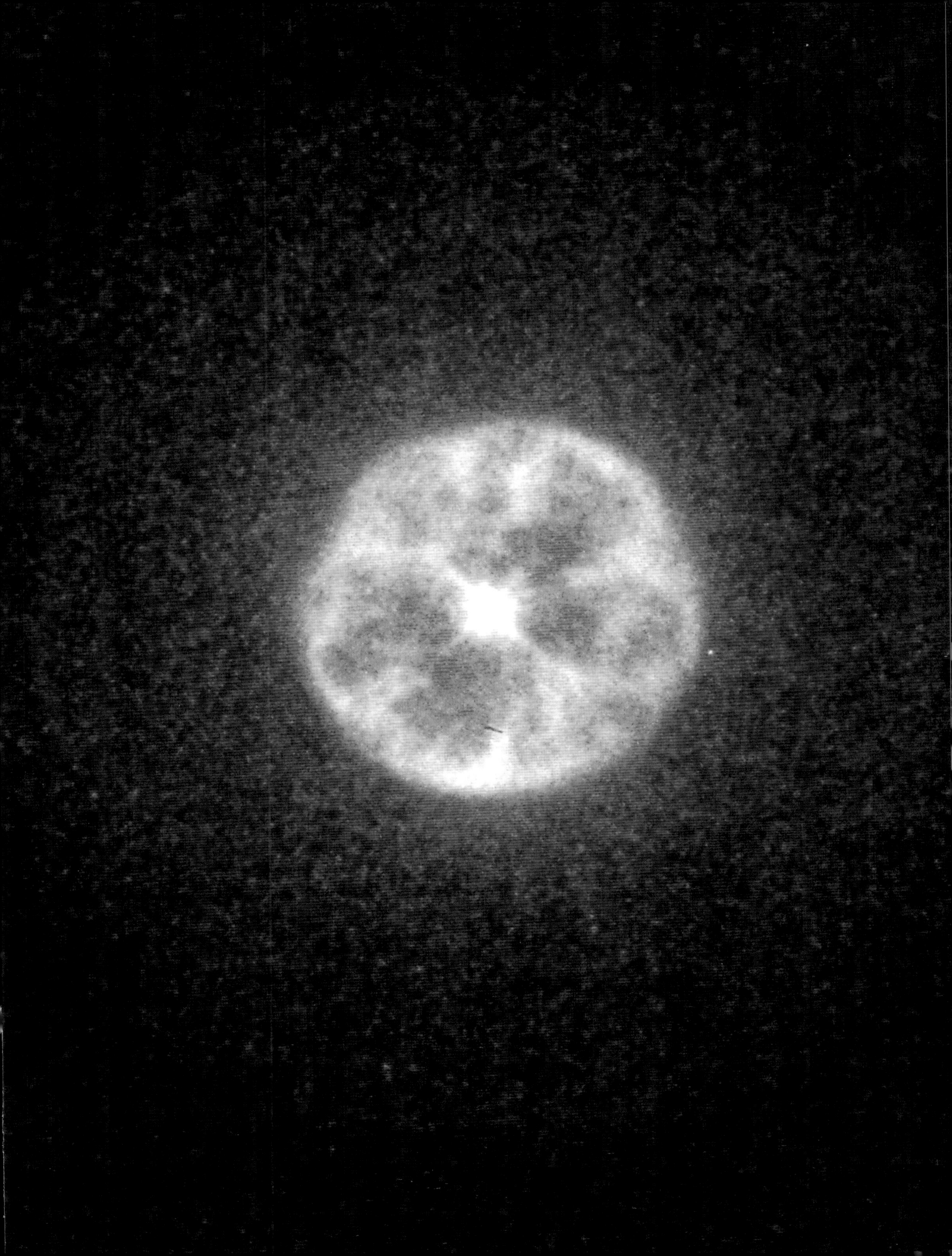

PLATE 21

PLANETARY NEBULA NGC 5307

In the constellation Centaurus lies the planetary nebula NGC 5307. This one has a symmetric appearance, each blob of gas having a twin on the other side of the star. The diameter of NGC 5307 is about 0.6 light years. At its distance of 10 000 light years, this makes it only 12 arcseconds across, the size of a 5 pence piece 170 metres away. This is still quite large in comparison with some of the objects the Hubble Space Telescope is capable of looking at.

The pinwheel or spiral structure of the nebula may result from gas having been blown away from the star in particular directions. Alternatively, there may be dark gas all around the star, but the radiation from the star is shining out and lighting up the gas only in certain directions.

See glossary entries: arcsecond; light year; planetary nebula

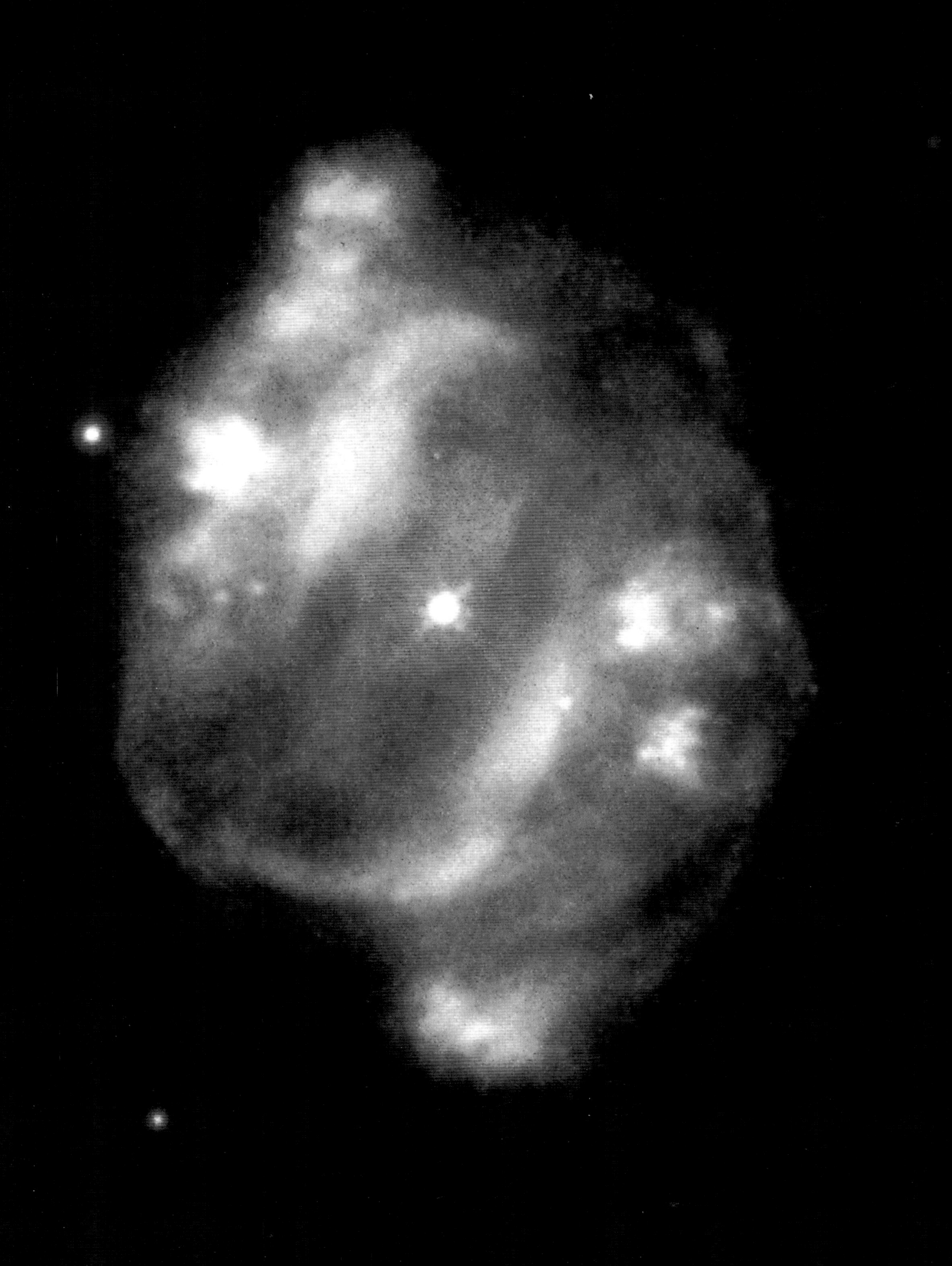

PLATE 22

PLANETARY NEBULA NGC 7009

NGC 7009 has an elongated appearance, including two 'handles' of low-density gas at either end. The bright central star can still be seen in the centre of the nebula in a cavity surrounded by the dense blue and red gas. NGC 7009 is 1400 light years away in the constellation Aquarius. Its complex shape is due in part to a number of different ejection episodes, material having been thrown out at different times.

All these pictures of planetary nebulae (Plates 19 to 28) were taken by WF/PC-2 – the Wide Field and Planetary Camera. The '2' indicates that it is a replacement for the original WF/PC. WF/PC-2 works together with COSTAR (Corrective Optics Space Telescope Axial Replacement), which contains special optics to correct for the flaw in the Hubble Space Telescope's mirror that was discovered only after launch in 1990. The mirror was ground 0.002 mm (that's one-fiftieth of the width of a human hair) too flat, enough to impair the performance of the telescope. WF/PC-2 was installed on the repair mission in 1993, and now the HST can observe to very nearly the accuracy of its original design.

See glossary entries: light year; planetary nebula; WF/PC

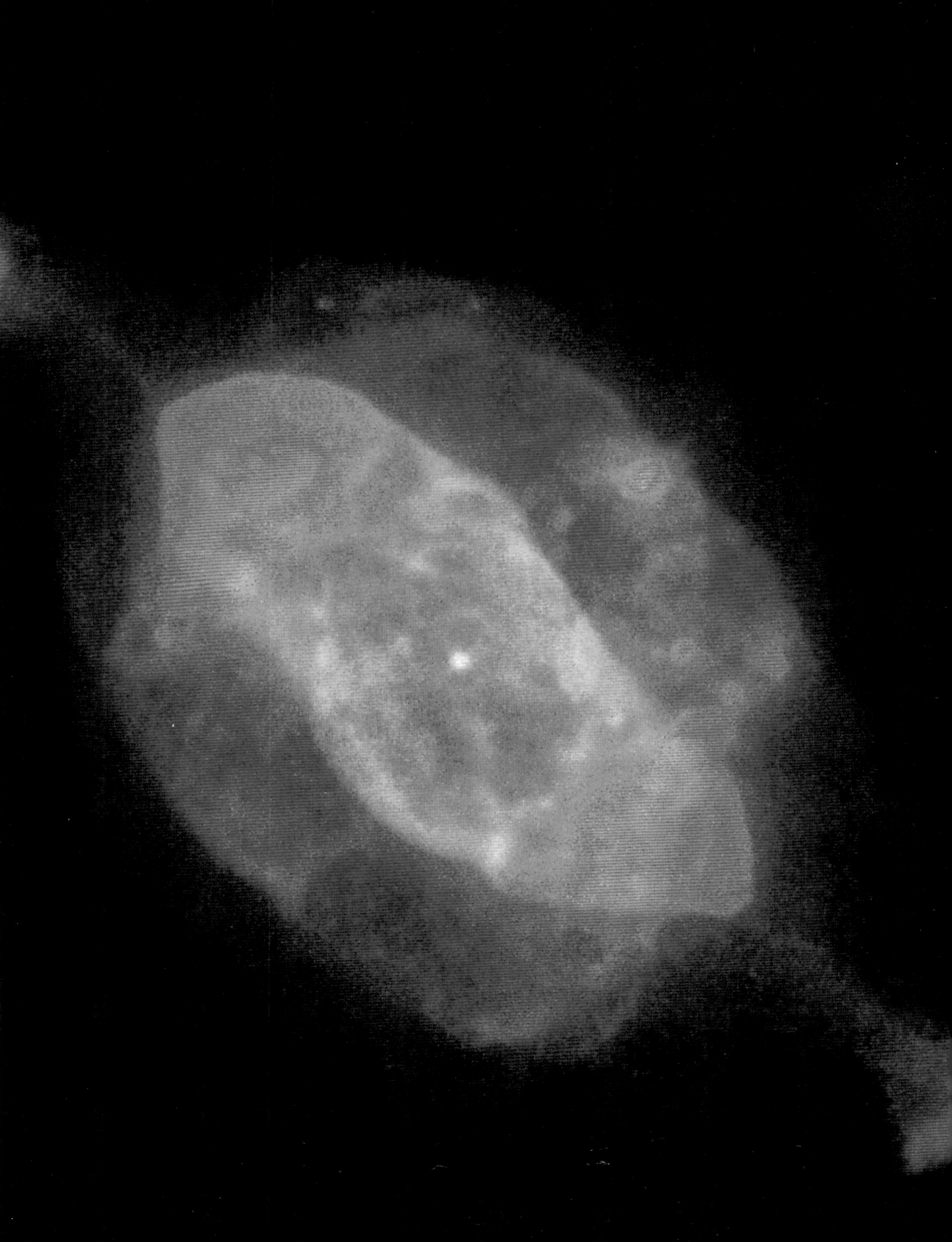

PLATE 23

THE STINGRAY: THE YOUNGEST PLANETARY NEBULA

The Stingray Nebula is the youngest known planetary nebula, probably only a few hundred years old. The star that shed the nebula can be seen in the centre of the picture, but close by (at 7 o'clock) a small companion star can be seen. This companion has a slight green 'tail' caused by a gravitational interaction with the material in the nebula.

Here the green colour is from oxygen, while the red is produced by nitrogen. The central star, like all stars, is producing a wind of small particles moving away from it at high speed. Gas is heated as the wind hits the inside of the bubble of ejected gas, causing some nitrogen atoms to lose one of their outer electrons. It is then said to be ionized. Different kinds of atom (atoms of different chemical elements) produce characteristic colours of light when heated.

The Stingray Nebula is 18 000 light years away, in the constellation Ara in the southern sky.

See glossary entries: light year; planetary nebula

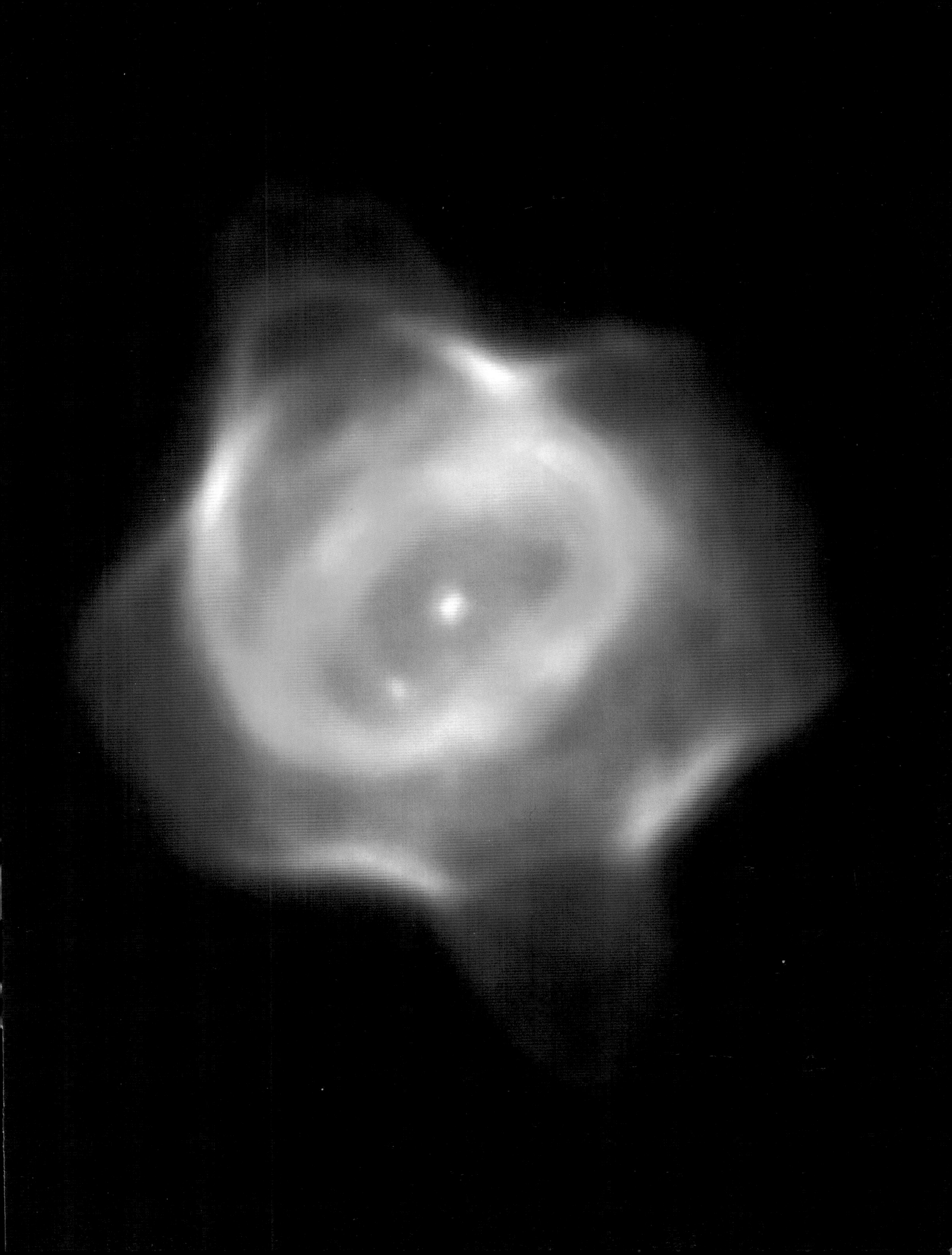

PLATE 24

THE EGG NEBULA

This is a view of the Egg Nebula, the planetary nebula CRL 2688, taken with NICMOS in infrared light. The colours in this image represent infrared light from different sources. The blue comes from regions of the nebula where starlight is being reflected off dust particles, while the red light comes from glowing hydrogen.

Material from the star is being ejected at high speed along jets. This material is rich in carbon, nitrogen and oxygen, elements crucial to life. A star like the Sun will produce a small amount of these elements by nuclear fusion in its core. The star does not produce a large amount of energy when doing this, but the process is an important means of enriching the interstellar gas with these elements.

See glossary entry: planetary nebula

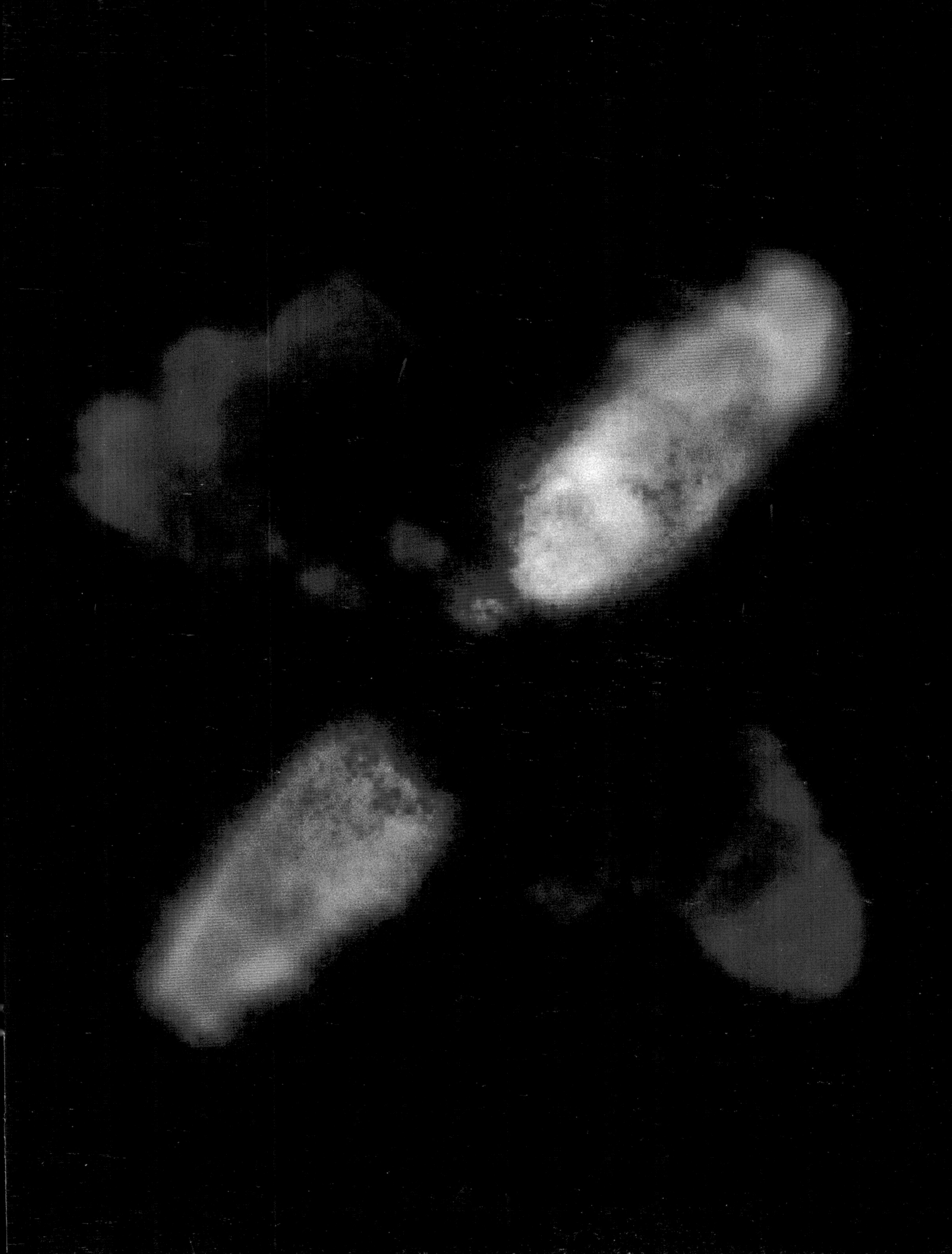

PLATE 25

PLANETARY NEBULA NGC 7027

This view of the planetary nebula NGC 7027 is a combination of images obtained in visible light and infrared light, using WF/PC-2 and NICMOS together. The transition of colours from the bright white central region to the blue outer regions marks a transition in temperature from hot gas to cold, dusty gas.

NICMOS imaged the central star, visible as the white spot at the centre of this view. The planetary nebula stage of a star's evolution lasts only a few thousand years, while the outer layers are thrown off. When all these layers are shed, what is left is the naked core of the star, a white dwarf. Gravity has crushed the core of the star, but it lacked sufficient mass to form a neutron star or black hole. Initially the white dwarf will be very hot, but it will slowly cool, dimming as it does so until it becomes invisible – a black dwarf.

See glossary entries: black dwarf; black hole; infrared light; neutron star; NICMOS; WF/PC

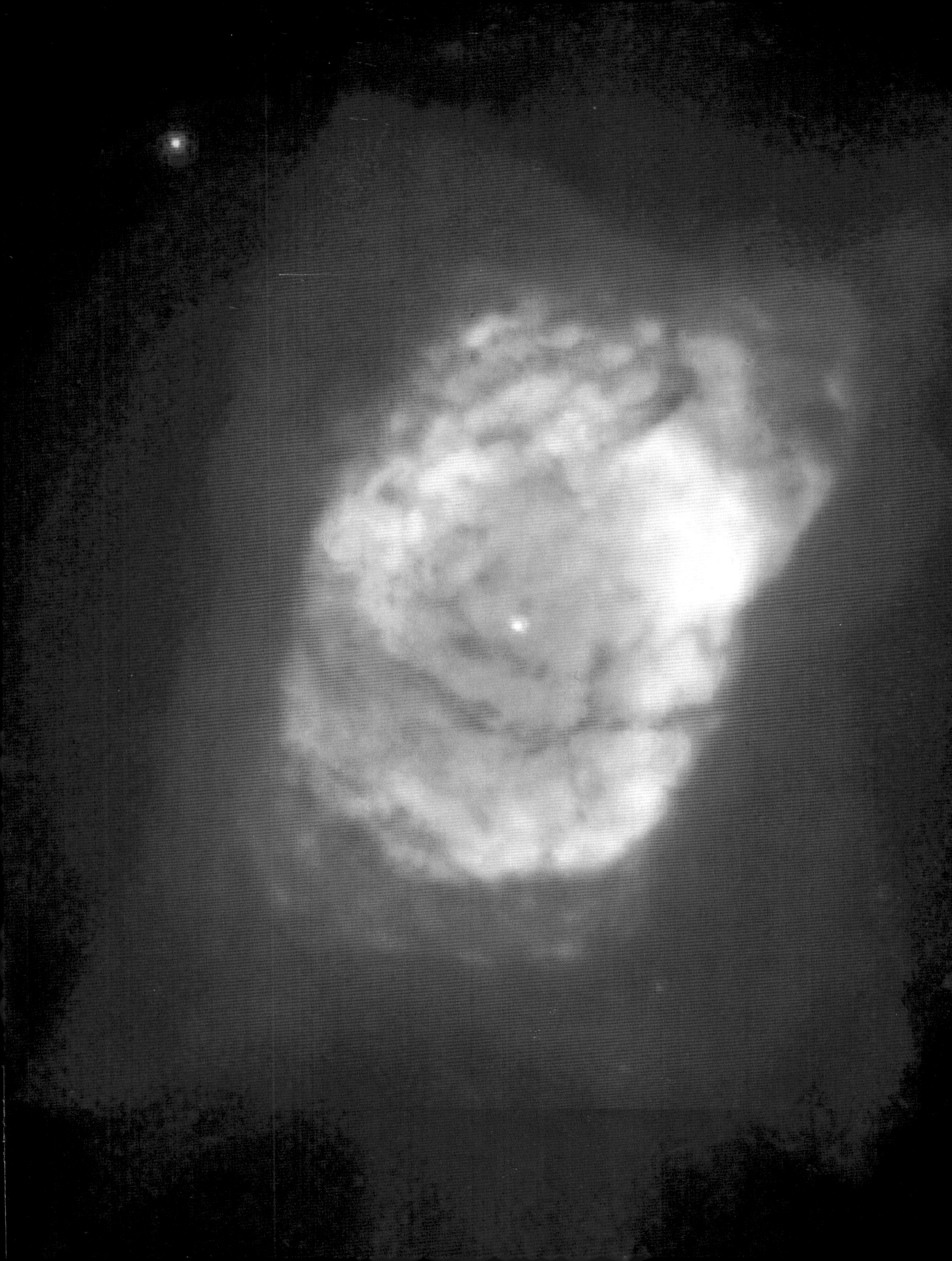

PLATE 26

A BUTTERFLY NEBULA

Not all planetary nebulae are roughly spherical: many show a bipolar symmetry, like M2-9, shown here. The gas in the two prominent jets was ejected at around a million km/h about 1200 years ago. It has not expanded into a spherical shell because the central star of M2-9 is not alone – it is one of a pair of stars that orbit very close together, so closely that the companion may even be inside the atmosphere of the central star. The companion is dragging a disk of gas and dust around with it, and this disk has prevented the planetary nebula from expanding in that direction. In this image the red comes from normal oxygen, the green from nitrogen that has lost one electron (slightly hotter gas) and the blue from oxygen that has lost two electrons (very hot gas).

Although not visible here, shorter exposures of the Hubble Space Telescope are able to record the disk, which has a diameter about 10 times that of Pluto's orbit around the Sun. M2-9 is 2100 light years away in the constellation Ophiuchus.

See glossary entries: binary system; light year; planetary nebula

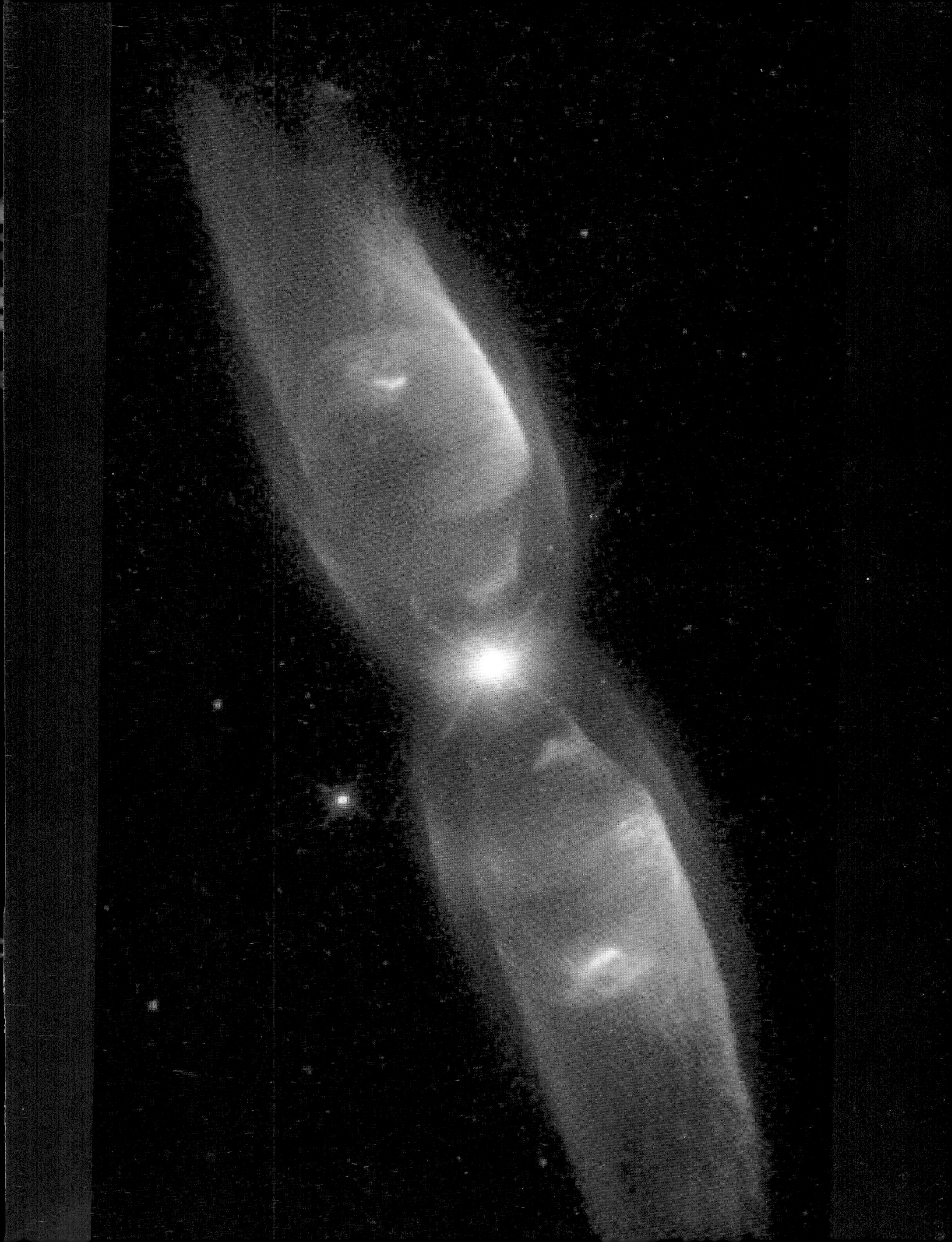

PLATE 27

TURTLE IN SPACE: NGC 6210

This planetary nebula, which has been likened to a turtle, has a very complex structure. What is interesting about NGC 6210 is the numerous holes in the shell from which material is streaming out. These holes may have been formed by dense blobs of material ejected from the central star, punching their way through the larger shell. Through these holes the hot stellar wind from the star can then escape.

The red and green colours in this image represent two different types of oxygen at different temperatures. The green is from oxygen that has lost one of its electrons, while the red is from oxygen without two of its electrons. The second electron is lost when the temperature is higher, so these colours show the temperature structure of the inner nebula. This inner region of the planetary nebula is half a light year across, but the whole nebula (the outer regions are not shown here) is larger, at 1.6 light years across.

See glossary entries: light year; planetary nebula

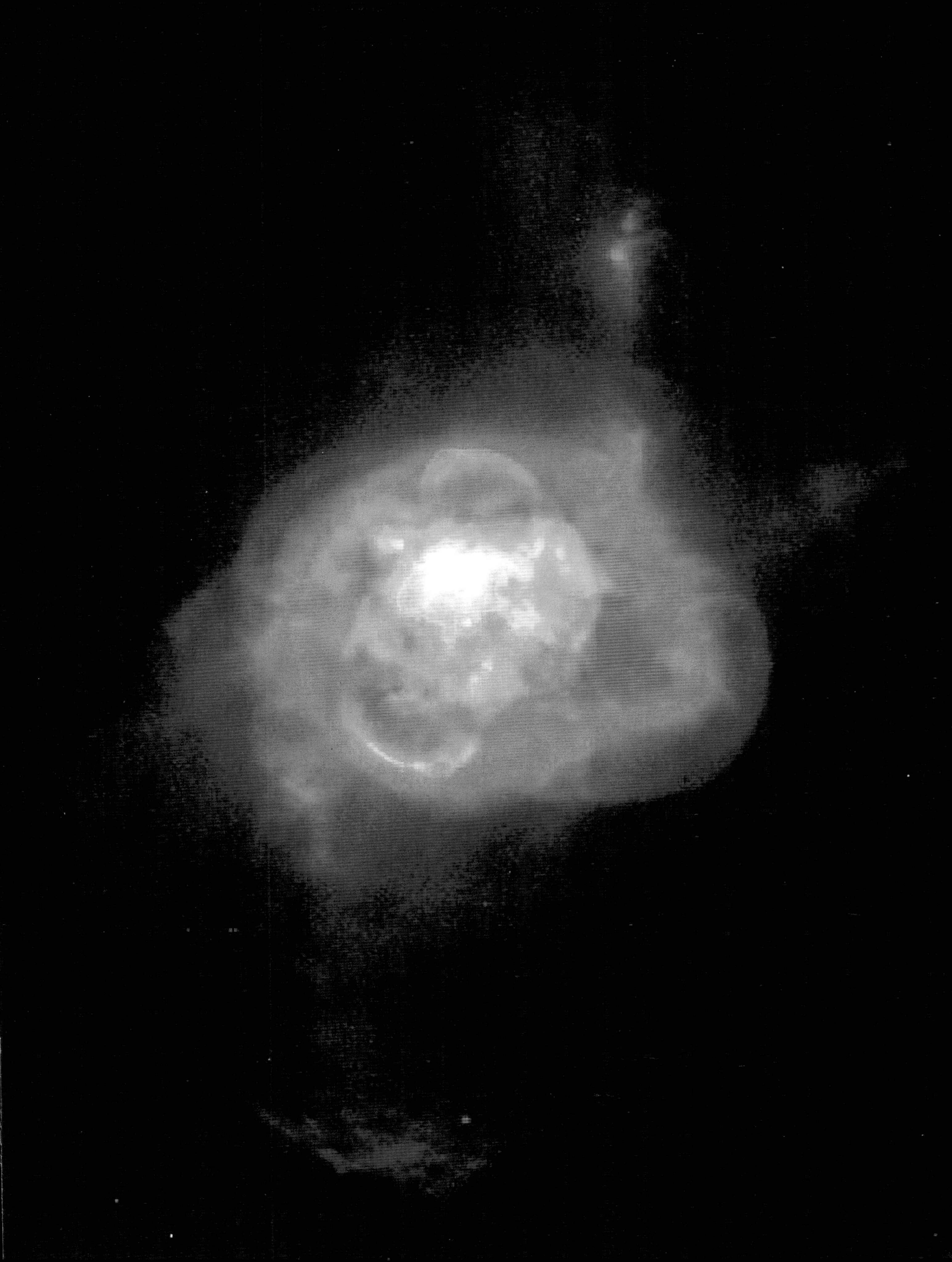

PLATE 28

COMETARY KNOTS IN THE HELIX NEBULA, NGC 7293

This is a close-up of a nearby planetary nebula. The Helix Nebula is only 450 light years away, and began forming around 10 000 years ago. The knots in this picture are huge structures on the inside of the nebula. Each blob is at least twice the size of the Solar System, and the 'tails' stretch for around 150 billion km. Cometary knots have no association with comets, and get their name simply from a passing resemblance. Astronomers do sometimes gives things confusing names – as with 'planetary' nebulae.

Cometary knots form when the ejected shell of material collides with cool interstellar gas. It may be that in the centres of each of these blobs Earth-sized objects can condense, formed from dust and ice. If so, the Galaxy may be filled with trillions of small planet-like objects wandering between the stars.

See glossary entries: light year; planetary nebula

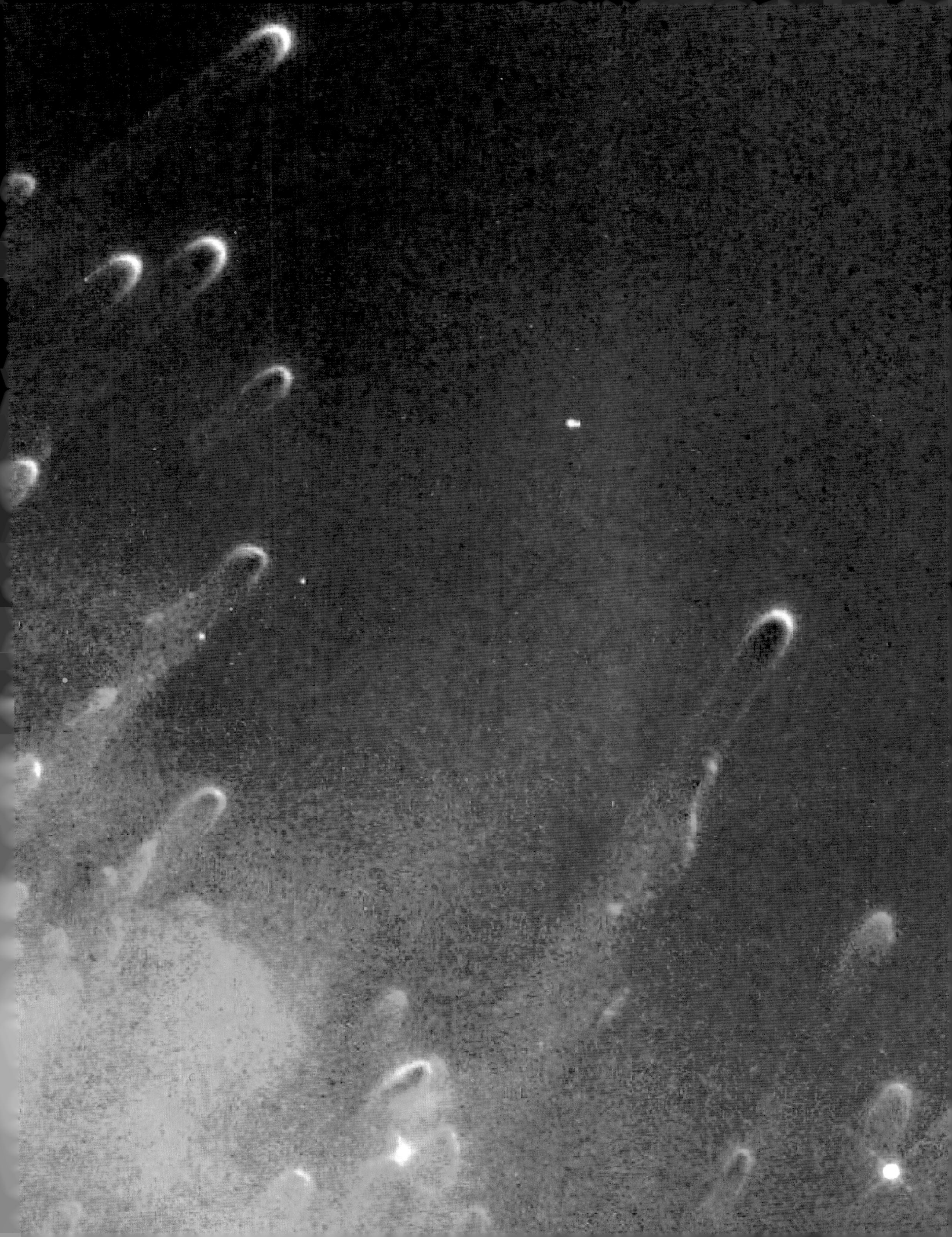

PLATE 29

THE BUBBLE NEBULA, NGC 7635

Shown here is part of the Bubble Nebula, so called because it is literally a huge bubble, 10 light years across, blasted out of the interstellar gas by the bright star at the left in this picture. The central star is around 10 or 20 times as massive as the Sun, nearly as big as the star that produced supernova SN 1987A (Plate 18). It will eventually go supernova itself in the next few tens of millions of years.

The intense radiation from the massive star, combined with an incredibly strong stellar wind of high-velocity particles, is pushing away the surrounding gas and heating it up at the same time. It is also responsible for the strange features at the bottom right-hand corner, similar to the cometary knots in Plate 28.

See glossary entries: light year; supernova

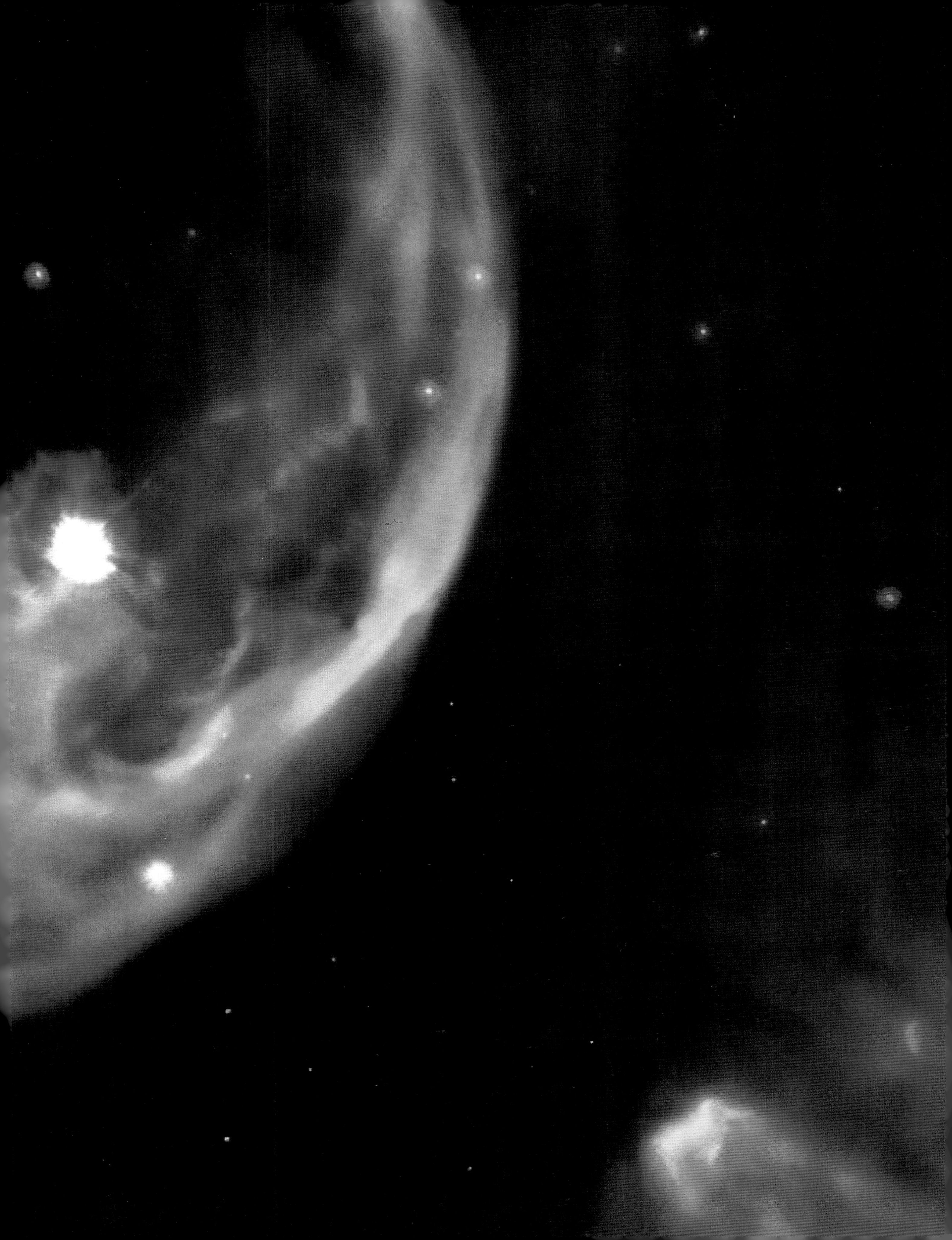

PLATE 30

NOVA T PYXIDIS

In a binary system which pairs a white dwarf with a normal star, it is possible for the white dwarf to drag material from the other star onto its surface. This material builds up over time and can sometimes be blasted off in a thermonuclear explosion. The system will then suddenly increase in brightness, and is known as a nova (Latin for 'new'), as an apparently new star can thus appear in the sky.

T Pyxidis, shown here, is a recurrent nova, undergoing frequent eruptions (five observed since 1890). The material that is blasted into space is not smoothly distributed. This image, taken with WF/PC-2, shows that there are more than 2000 blobs of material within 1 light year of the nova. It is not known whether these blobs are blasted out by the explosion of the nova, or whether they form when the hot ejected gas collides with cooler interstellar gas.

See glossary entries: light year; nova; WF/PC; white dwarf

PLATE 31

RED DWARF GLIESE 623b

If a blob of matter condensing out of a nebula has less than about a tenth of the mass of the Sun, its central temperature and pressure will never get high enough for the fusion of hydrogen into helium to begin, and it will fail to achieve stellar status. The star Gliese 623b is almost right at this limit of being a star. It is 60 000 times fainter than the Sun, so faint that if it were at the same distance from us as the Sun it would shine only eight times brighter than the full Moon. This picture shows it for the first time.

Gliese 623b is a red dwarf star orbiting its Sun-like companion at only twice the Earth–Sun distance. Since the pair lie only 25 light years away, the Hubble Space Telescope was able to resolve the two stars and show them separately.

Red dwarfs are the most numerous stars in the Universe, but they are so faint as to be invisible at any great distance from us. This picture was taken by the HST's Faint Object Camera (replaced in the 1997 servicing mission), an instrument specially designed to observe extremely dim objects. The FOC was replaced, not because it had stopped working but because the space was needed for new instruments that could observe different things.

See glossary entries: light year; red dwarf; Sun

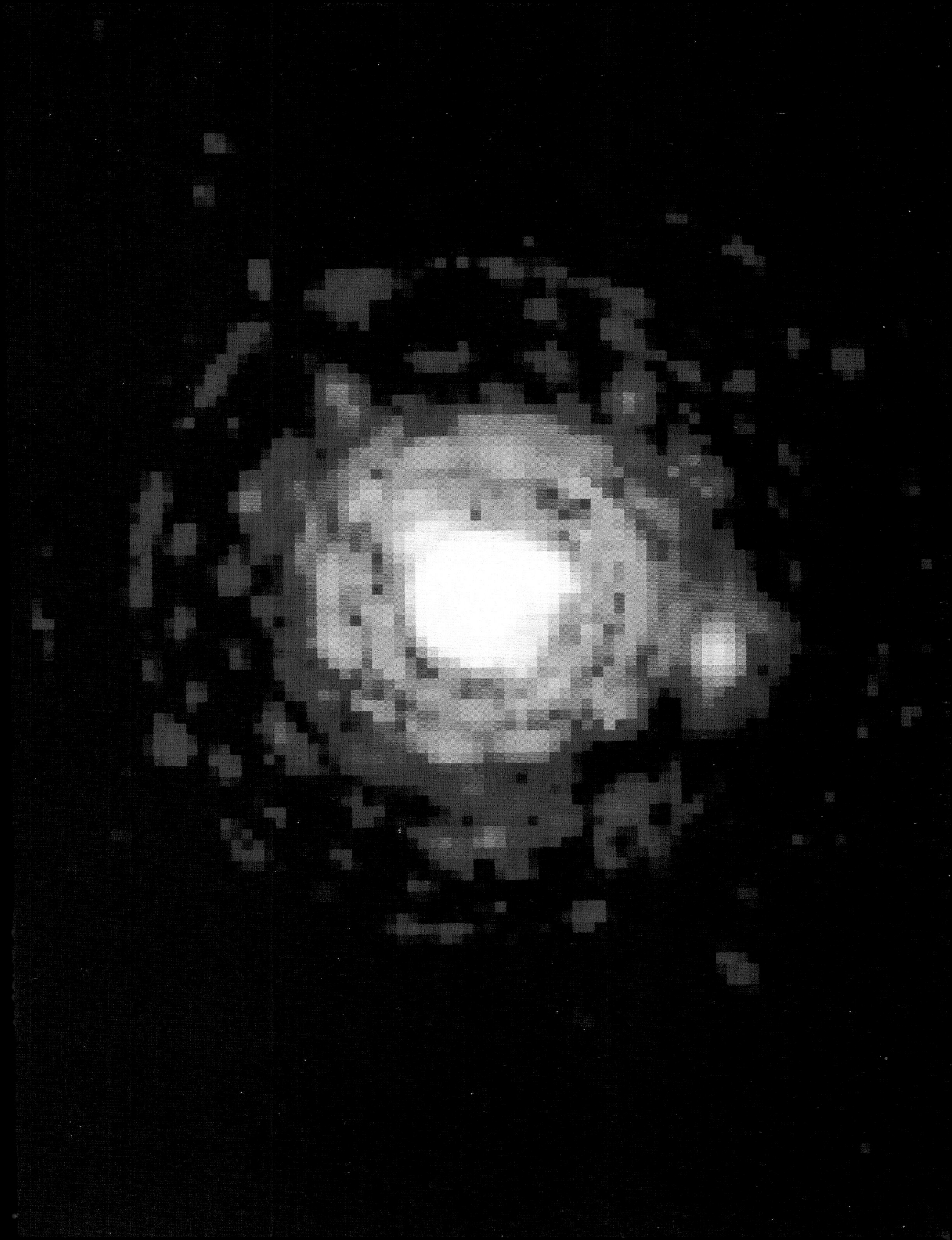

PLATE 32

GLIESE 105c: THE SMALLEST STAR?

Gliese 105c is an even smaller star than Gliese 623b (Plate 31). This star is right at the borderline of red dwarfs and what are known as brown dwarfs. Brown dwarfs do not shine by nuclear energy, but produce a small amount of infrared radiation from the heat left over from their initial gravitational contraction. The dividing line between a brown dwarf and a planet such as Jupiter is not clear, and it can be argued that Jupiter is just a small brown dwarf star.

This image was taken in visible and infrared light. The predominantly red colour of Gliese 105c shows that it is much cooler than its companion star (which itself is smaller than the Sun). The white bars across the larger star are caused by the optics of the telescope and the CCD camera, and are not real.

See glossary entries: binary system; brown dwarf; charge coupled device; infrared light; planet; red dwarf

PLATE 33

THE DISK OF BETA PICTORIS

This image shows a disk of gas and dust around the nearby star Beta Pictoris. The full disk is 220 billion km (1500 astronomical units) in diameter and tilted so that we are looking at it almost edge-on. This picture is a close-up of the inner 2 billion km, smaller than the Solar System. The light from Beta Pictoris itself has been blotted out from the middle so that details of the disk can be seen.

It is thought that the planets in our Solar System formed from a disk such as this around the young Sun, slowly condensing out of the disk and accreting into larger and larger bodies.

The warping and twisting of the Beta Pictoris disk are thought by some astronomers to be evidence that planets exist inside the disk. Any planets would be hidden from view by the dusty disk, but even if they were not they would be too faint to see.

See glossary entries: astronomical unit; planet

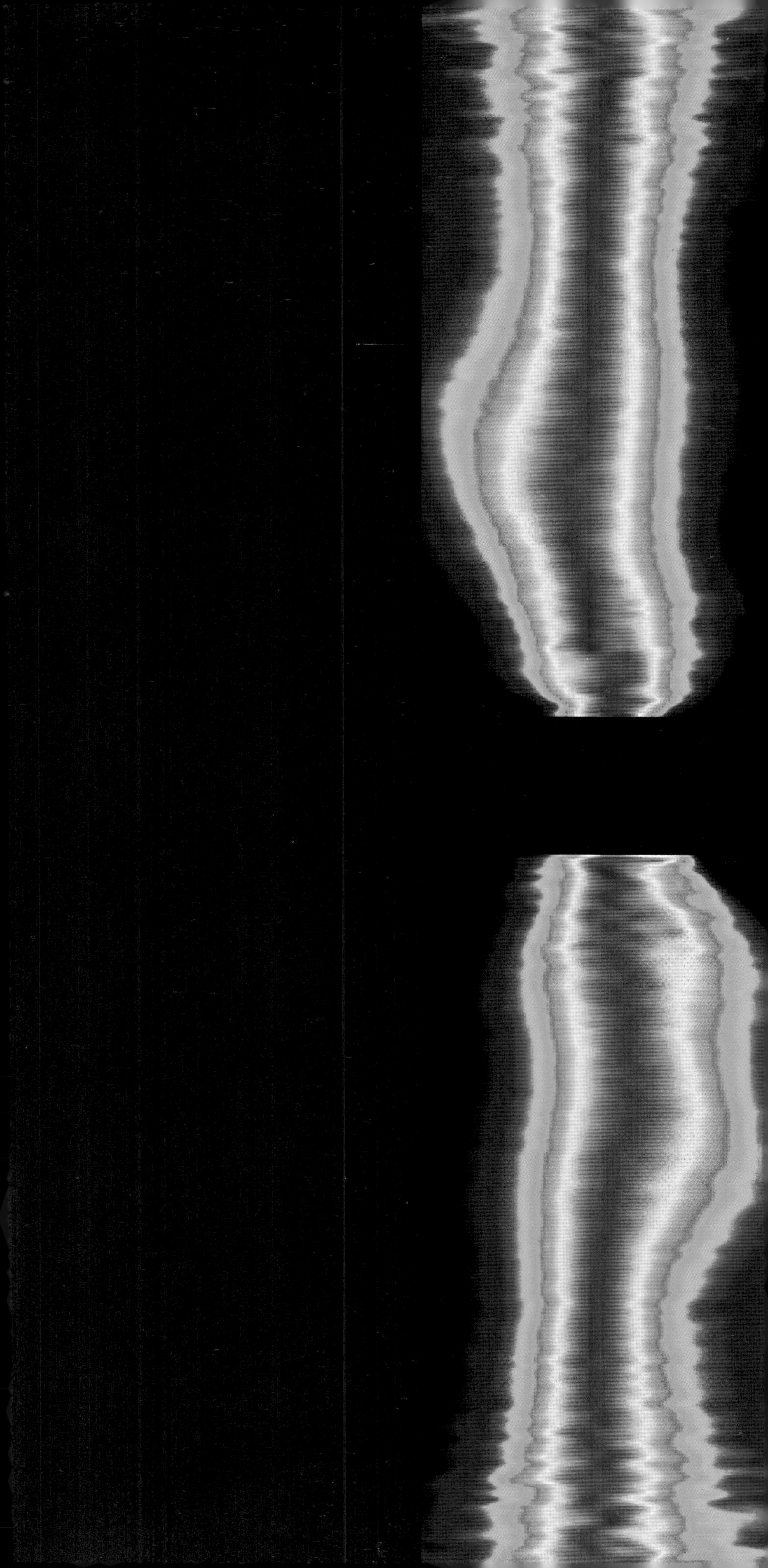

PLATE 34

YOUNG STELLAR DISKS

Disks around young stars like Beta Pictoris do not seem to be a rare phenomenon. Here we see two young stars surrounded by dusty disks tens of billions of kilometres across. The Hubble Space Telescope has discovered many hundreds of disks around young stars, many in the Orion Nebula (Plates 3 and 4).

The discovery of these disks is of great importance in assessing how common planets may be in the Galaxy. For planets to form, a disk must be present, although it is not known whether a disk will always spawn planets. That there are disks around many young stars suggests that planet formation may well be a fairly common process.

These images were taken by WF/PC-2 in visible light.

See glossary entries: astronomical unit; planet; WF/PC

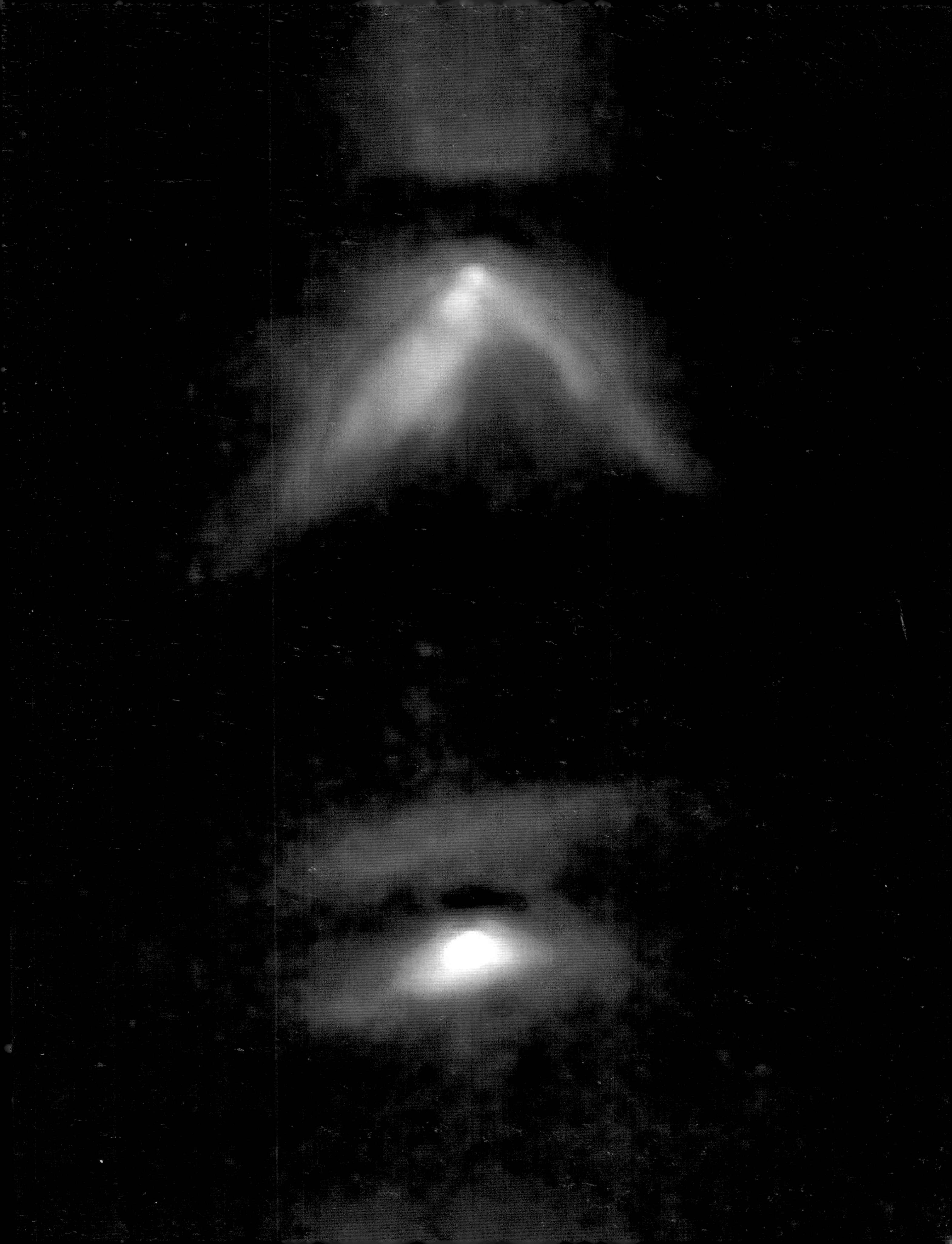

PLATE 35

DISKS IN THE INFRARED

These images show the protoplanetary disks in Plate 34 – DG Tau B and Haro 6-5B – obtained this time by using NICMOS to look in the infrared. NICMOS has been able to penetrate the dust surrounding the young stars, and see more than WF/PC-2 looking in visible light.

The jets from DG Tau B are visible only in the infrared image, where they can be seen shooting out 140 billion km from the poles of the central star, at right angles to the disk. The infrared image also shows a wispy gas structure around Haro 6-5B, and gives away the location of the star from the tiny green jet it is emitting.

Some 5 billion years ago the young Sun probably looked similar to DG Tau B and Haro 6-5B. Understanding these stars will tell us what the Sun was like when it first formed, as well as providing clues as to how stars form – one of the central problems in astrophysics.

See glossary entries: infrared light; NICMOS; Sun; WF/PC

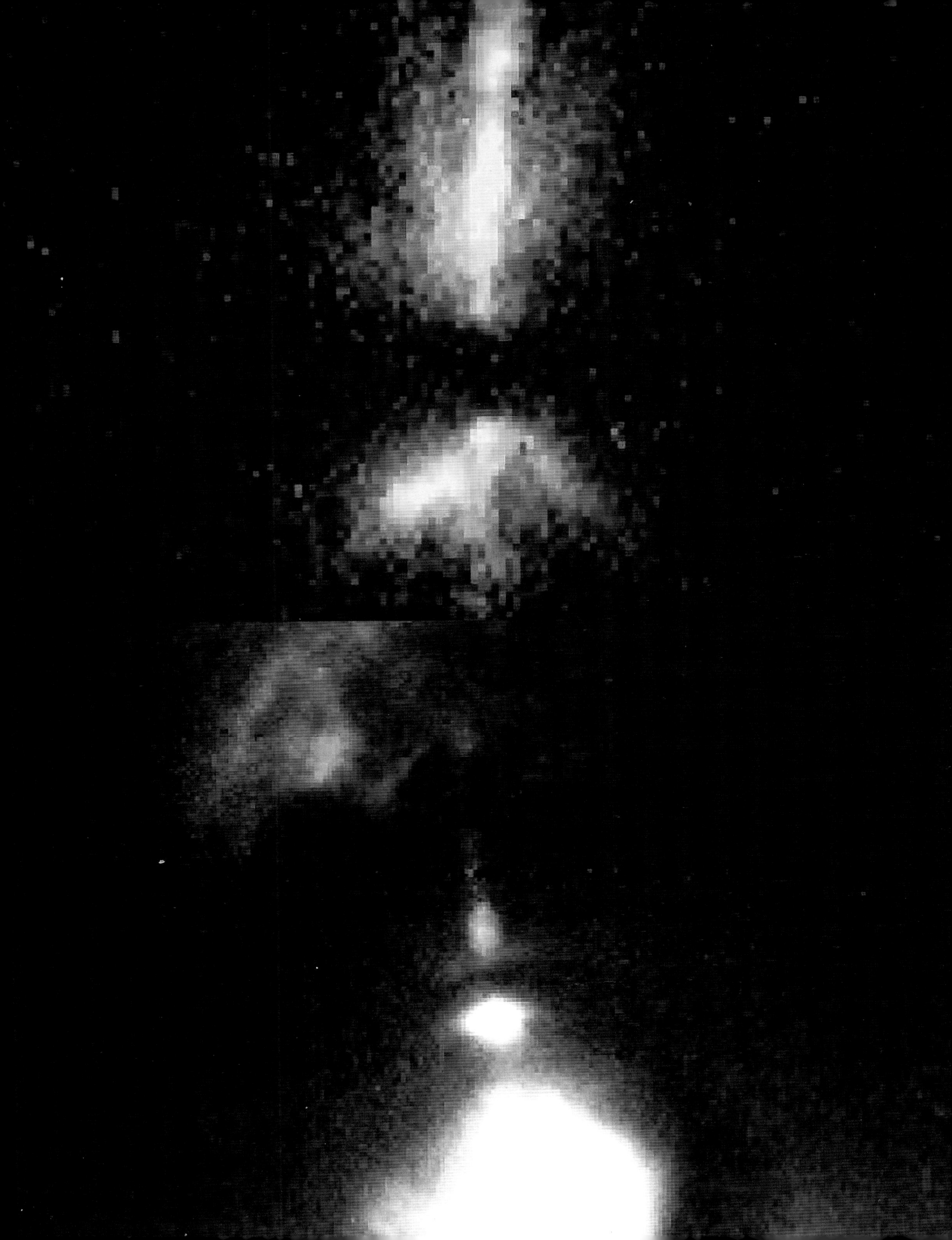

PLATE 36

ANOTHER PLANET?

At the centre of this picture are two very young stars in a binary pair, surrounded by a cloud of gas and dust. Towards the bottom left of the picture, though, is possibly our first glimpse of a planet outside our Solar System.

The brightness of this object shows that it is much too small to be a red dwarf, and it has a mass only several times that of Jupiter. Much depends on where we draw the line between brown dwarfs and planets, but this may well be classifiable as a planet. The stream of material between the young binary and the planet suggest that it was probably ejected from the young system.

Planets cool as they age, having no source of energy, so it is only the very young age of this planet that allows us to see it as it glows slightly in the infrared. Its distance of 200 billion km from the binary pair also makes it far easier to see, as it is not swamped by their light.

See glossary entries: binary system; brown dwarf; infrared light; planet; red dwarf

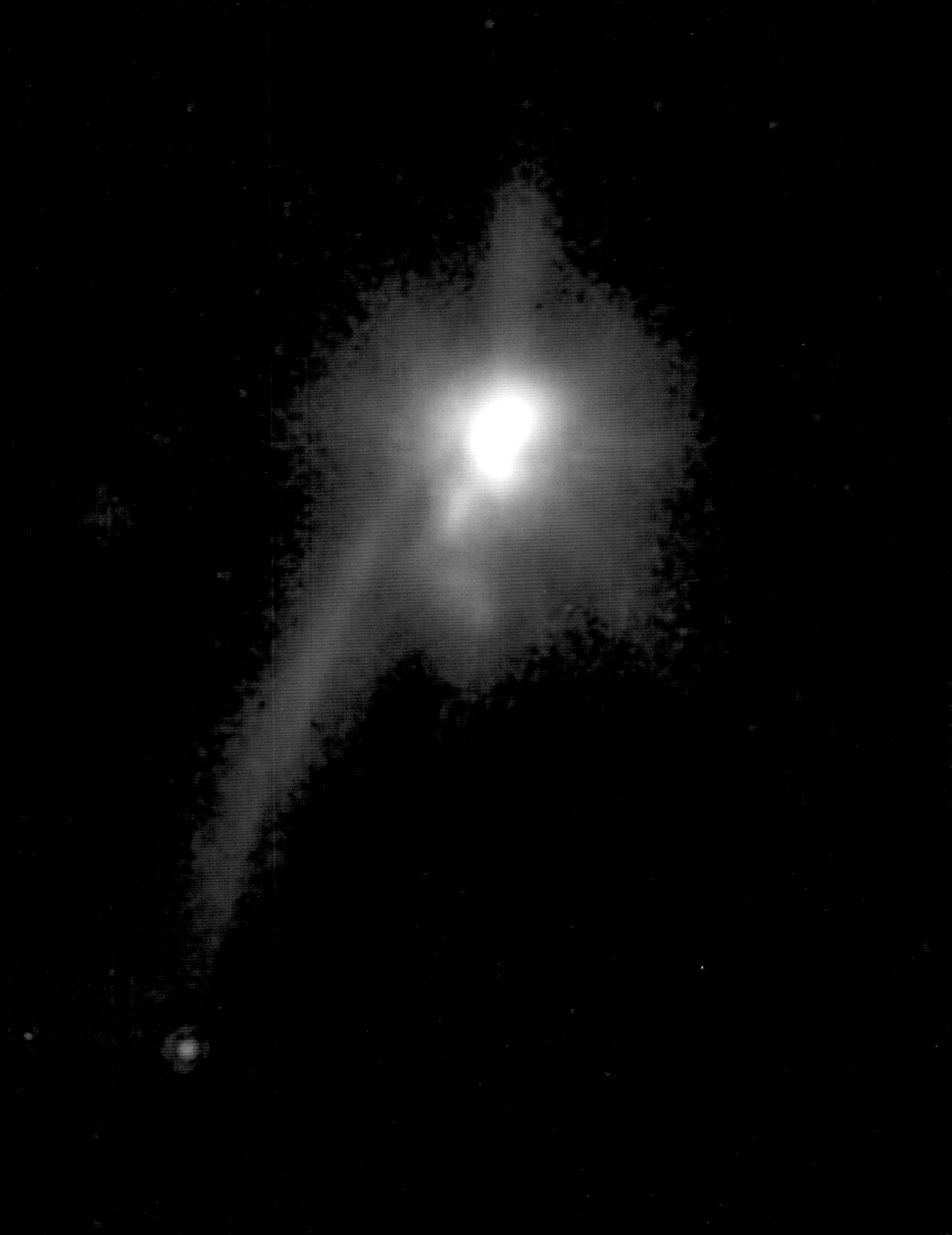

PLATE 37

THE HUBBLE DEEP FIELD

So far we have concentrated on the local Universe, on stars and nebulae in the Milky Way and other nearby galaxies. The wider visible Universe is big – roughly 15 billion light years in radius – and contains hundreds of billions of galaxies, each containing hundreds of billions of stars. This is an image taken using WF/PC-2 in 1995 in infrared and visible light, and shows the true colours of galaxies (if we were able to see objects this faint, that is).

One of the most intriguing features of astronomy on this scale is the way our telescopes act as time machines. Because we see galaxies millions of light years away, we see them as they were millions of years ago, when the light we are seeing them by started out on its journey to the Earth. By comparing galaxies at different distances, we can see how the Universe as a whole has evolved since the Big Bang in which it was born.

This picture is a snapshot of the Universe, and shows objects that are as much as 2 billion times fainter than the faintest naked-eye stars we can see in the night sky. The portion of the sky in this image, known as the Hubble Deep Field (HDF), is the same size as a pea held at arm's length, yet it contains thousands of identifiable objects, all of which are galaxies. The HDF lies in the northern section of the constellation Ursa Major, just below the border with Draco.

See glossary entries: age of the Universe; galaxy; light year; look-back time; WF/PC

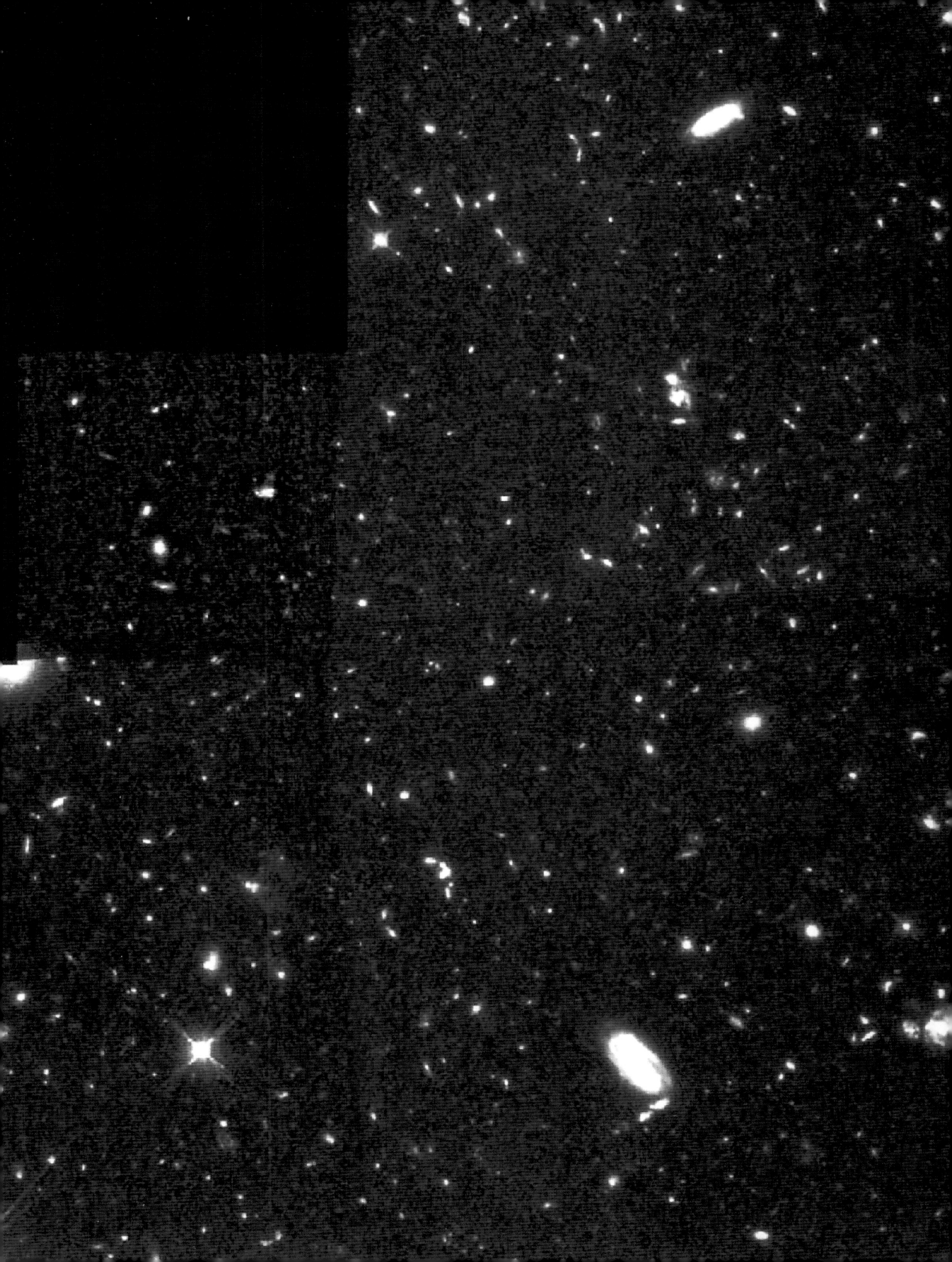

PLATE 38

BARRED SPIRAL GALAXY NGC 4639

This galaxy, NGC 4639, lies 78 million light years away and belongs to the Virgo Cluster of galaxies, the nearest large concentration of galaxies to us. The Milky Way and the other galaxies of the Local Group (our own 'mini cluster' of galaxies) is being dragged towards the Virgo Cluster at around 500 000 km/h, tugged by the gravitational pull of the cluster.

NGC 4639 is a barred spiral galaxy. Bright spiral arms can be seen emanating from a bar extending from the bright central nucleus. The Milky Way would probably look something like this if we were able to look down upon it from some distant vantage point.

We know that our Galaxy is flattened, as the bright band of the Milky Way (which gave it its name) in the sky shows. From the southern hemisphere it is possible to see the central bulge as a large concentration of stars in the sky crossed by thick dust lanes. We also think that the Milky Way has a bar structure in the middle, although probably not as pronounced as in NGC 4639.

See glossary entries: light year; Milky Way; spiral galaxy

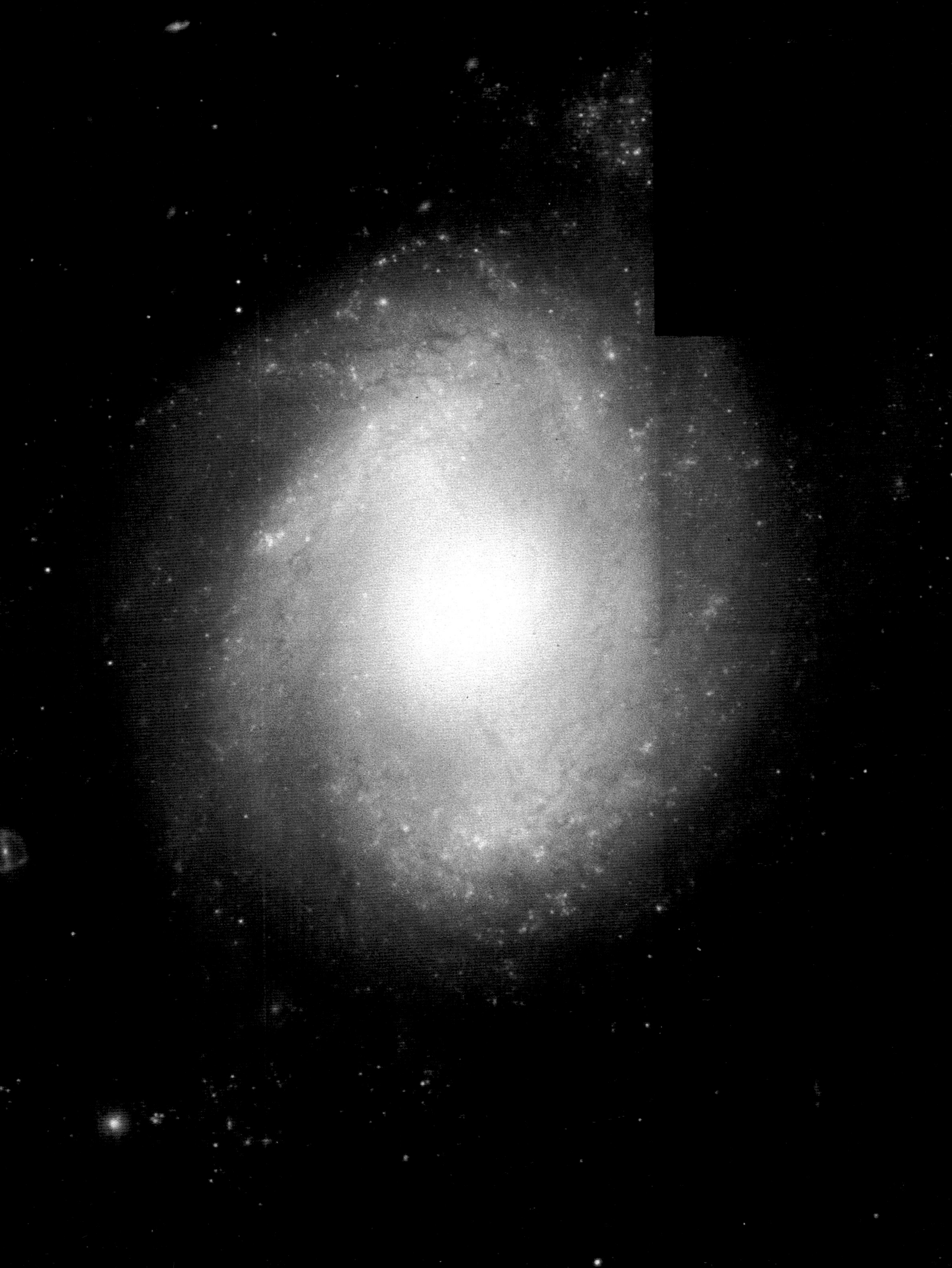

PLATE 39

CEPHEIDS IN THE GALAXY NGC 1365

One of the most difficult things in astronomy is finding the distance to galaxies. The method used most often is to find a 'standard candle' – an object whose brightness we think we know (from studies of similar objects nearby) in a distant galaxy. Seeing how faint the standard candle looks in the galaxy tells us how far away the galaxy is (since the brightness of objects tails off in proportion to the square of their distance).

The best standard candles are Cepheid variable stars: bright, pulsating stars whose brightness is proportional to how fast they pulsate. Observing Cepheids in distant galaxies to determine the period of their brightness changes is one of the main jobs of the Hubble Space Telescope, and so far it has enabled astronomers to establish the distances to about 20 galaxies. Previously, accurate distance were available for only three galaxies, all very close to us.

The HST observed 50 Cepheids in NGC 1365, and its distance was found to be about 60 million light years. These Cepheids lie along the bottom edge of this WF/PC-2 image, though unfortunately they are invisible without special processing.

See glossary entries: Cepheid variable; distance scale of the Universe; galaxy; light year; spiral galaxy; WF/PC

PLATE 40

SPIRAL GALAXY NGC 4314

NGC 4314 is another spiral galaxy, 40 million light years away. Its unusual feature is a bright ring around the central nucleus, a ring 2000 light years in diameter in which stars are forming. For some reason, this ring is the only place in NGC 4314 in which stars are forming at all.

This image is a combination of light in the infrared, visible and ultraviolet regions of the spectrum. The purple light is from hydrogen heated by the radiation from massive young stars. The yellow is light from older, smaller stars, and it is just possible to make out the spiral arms of this galaxy.

Star-forming regions are easy to see as they contain massive bright stars. Since massive stars do not live for very long, their very existence tells us that there has been very recent star formation. Most of the stars that are forming here are probably red dwarfs, but they are so faint in comparison with the massive stars that their light is insignificant. Much of the star formation in this ring took place less than 5 million years before the light by which we see it left NGC 4314. But the light has been so long on its journey that most of the massive stars in the ring will have burned out by now.

See glossary entries: infrared light; light year; red dwarf; ultraviolet light

PLATE 41

STARBURST GALAXY NGC 253

Lying 8 million light years away in the constellation Sculptor is the galaxy NGC 253. The central region of NGC 253 is seen undergoing a starburst, an intense episode of star formation which occurs in some galaxies.

This WF/PC-2 image shows the disk of NGC 253 tilted at a slight angle to us. In the core of the galaxy is a bright yellow region surrounded by dark clouds of gas and dust: this is the starburst. The image has the unmistakable staircase profile of a WF/PC-2 image. The smaller square in the top left is the field of view of the planetary camera (a quarter the size of the three wide-field cameras), which was centred on the starburst to allow that region to be studied in more detail.

The star-forming region does not show the normal bright blue colours expected from massive stars (as in Plate 40). The reason for this is that the star-forming region is still shrouded in dust and gas. The blue light coming from the massive young stars is absorbed by the surrounding gas and re-emitted as longer-wavelength light, appearing yellow in this picture.

See glossary entry: WF/PC

PLATE 42

DUST LANES IN CENTAURUS A

Centaurus A is an elliptical galaxy 10 million light years away. Unlike normal elliptical galaxies, which contain no gas, Centaurus A is girdled by a huge ring of gas and dust that is forming vast numbers of stars.

The cold dust and clouds of hydrogen are lit from behind by the glow of hot young stars. Above the dust lane in this image can be seen the hot blue glow of young star clusters similar to NGC 1818 (Plate 11).

This gas is thought to have come from a small spiral galaxy which Centaurus A cannibalized, shredding it and spreading its component gas and dust into the huge ring circling the giant elliptical galaxy. Behind the remains of the unfortunate spiral galaxy can be seen the hazy glow of Centaurus A's original population of older red stars.

See glossary entries: elliptical galaxy; spiral galaxy

PLATE 43

THE ANTENNAE GALAXIES, NGC 4038 AND 4039

Galactic cannibalism is not a very rare event. Galaxies encounter each other on a regular basis. Even our own Milky Way is in the process of consuming a galaxy (the Sagittarius Dwarf Galaxy, which unfortunately is on the other side of the Milky Way and cannot easily be studied from the Earth), and in a few billion years it will destroy the Large and Small Magellanic Clouds as well. These galaxies are small compared with the Milky Way, and their cannibalization will have little effect on the structure of the Milky Way. If two galaxies meet which are approximately the same size, however, the results can be dramatic.

The Antennae are two similar-sized spiral galaxies, NGC 4038 and 4039, which are undergoing a very close encounter. The remains of their original spiral structure can still be seen, especially the two large orange central bulges of the galaxies on either side in this picture. The disks and spiral arms of the two galaxies, though, are interacting, throwing up a tremendous amount of dust which can be seen as the dark obscuring patches in the centre of this image.

See glossary entries: dwarf galaxy; Milky Way; spiral galaxy

PLATE 44

CLOSE-UP OF THE ANTENNAE

This picture is a close-up of the core of NGC 4038, the bottom galaxy in Plate 43. Gas and dust are being funnelled into the core, fuelling a tremendous burst of star formation. The dust and gas are causing the bright young blue stars to look yellow and orange again, as in NGC 253 (Plate 41), and in some places they totally block out the light. Throughout the Antennae huge star clusters are being formed, each containing millions of stars.

Eventually, it is thought, the two galaxies of the Antennae will spiral together to make a single elliptical galaxy. The gas supplies of the two galaxies will quickly run out, consumed in star formation, and all that will be left will be a ball of smaller stars surrounded by globular clusters.

See glossary entries: elliptical galaxy; globular cluster

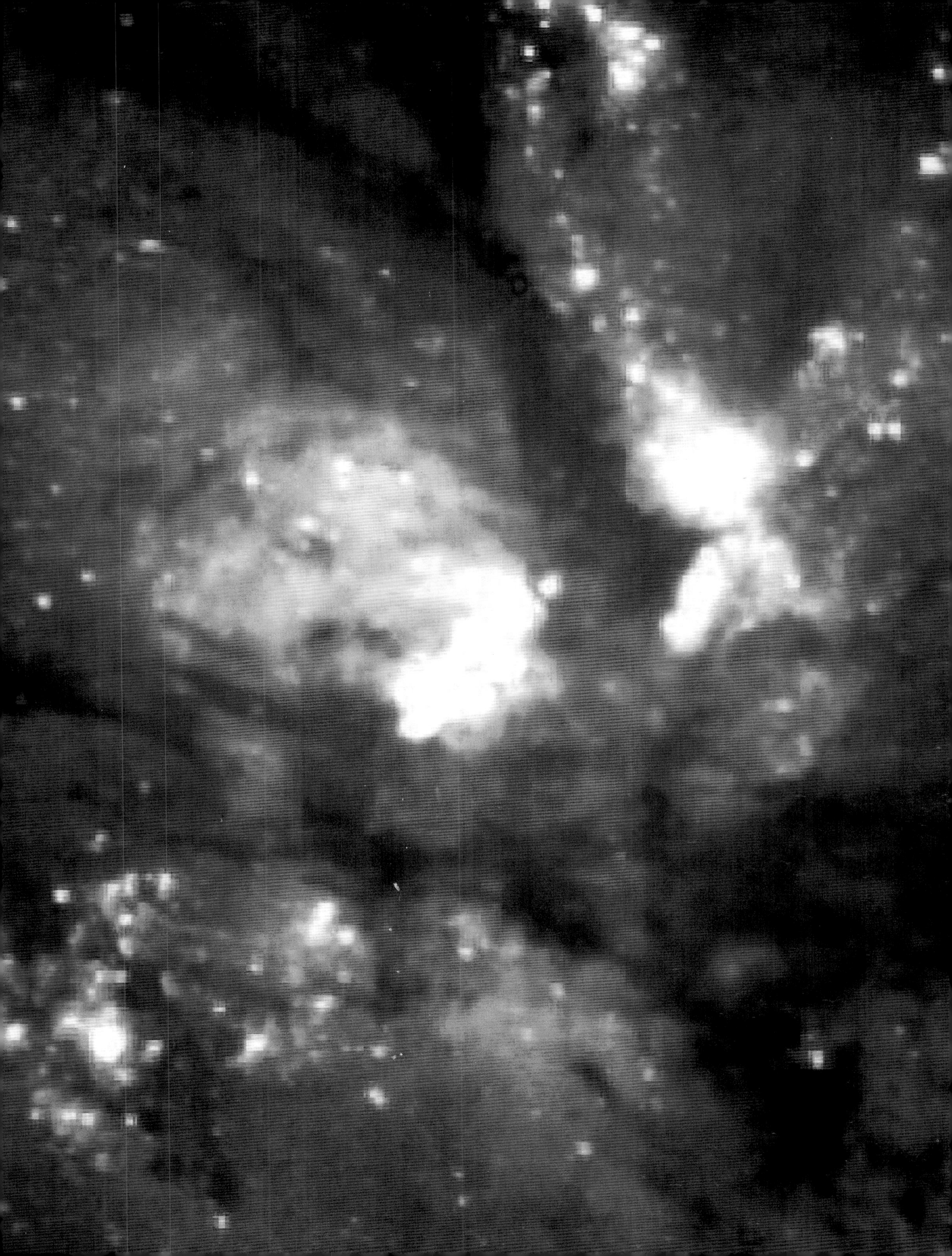

PLATE 45

DEEP IMPACT IN GALAXY ARP 220

The peculiar galaxy Arp 220 is 250 million light years away, and is part of astronomer Halton Arp's catalogue of unusual galaxies. The Hubble Space Telescope has used NICMOS to probe the centre of Arp 220, and discovered that it is probably the result of a galactic collision.

Peculiar and unusual galaxies are galaxies that do not fit easily into the definition of spiral and elliptical galaxies. Their shapes are most often very irregular, and they contain a lot of dust and gas. They do not have the symmetry of classical spirals and ellipticals, probably because they have suffered an encounter with another galaxy. Sometimes the galaxy that was encountered is nearby, sometimes it is long gone, and sometimes the other galaxy has been cannibalized by the irregular galaxy.

The cores of what once were two separate galaxies can be seen spiralling slowly towards each other; eventually they will coalesce into a single core. The motions of these cores are stimulating a lot of star formation in Arp 220, mixing gas and causing gas clouds to collide. The cores are also surrounded by a thick disk of gas and obscuring dust.

See glossary entries: elliptical galaxy; spiral galaxy

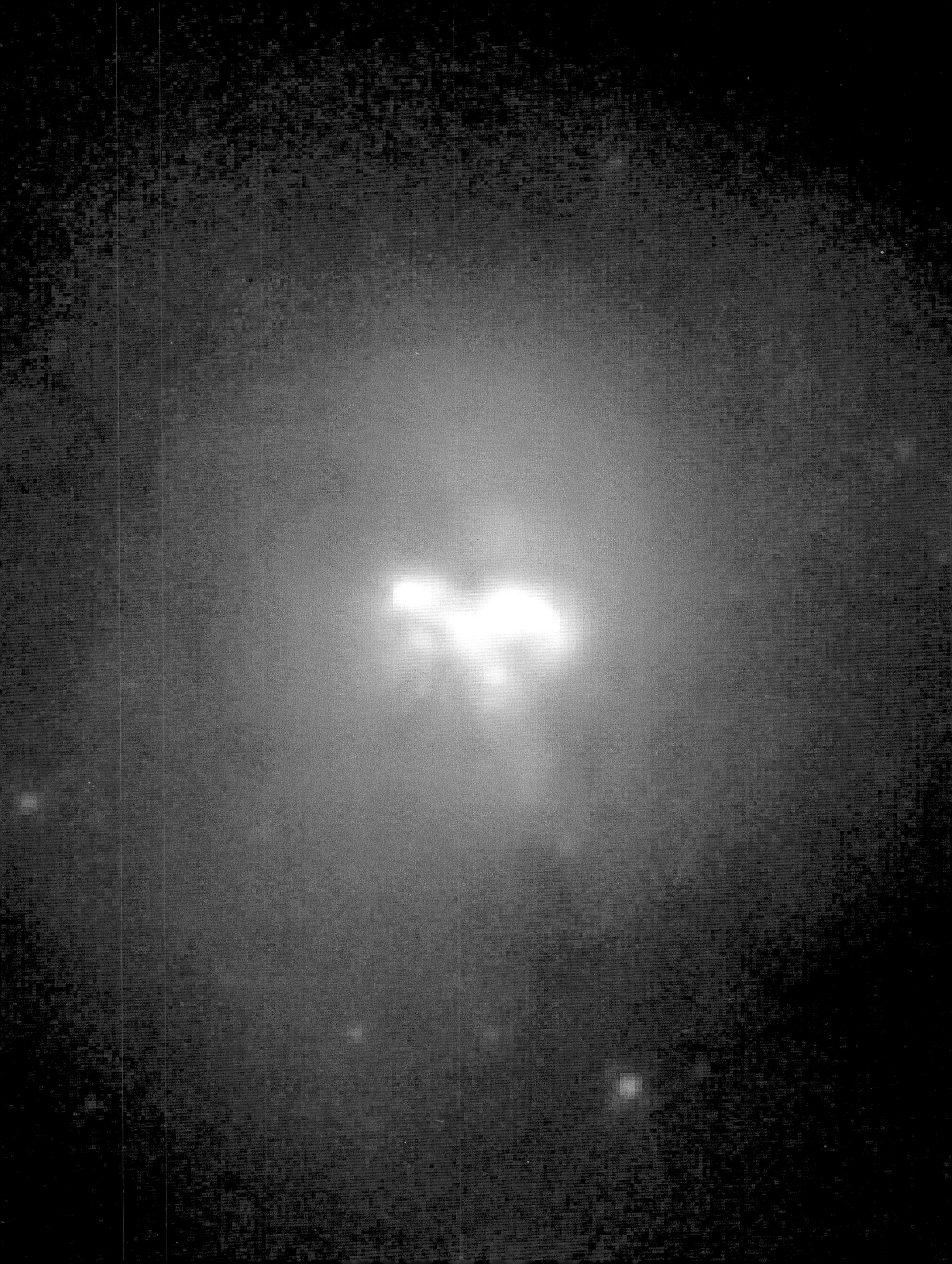

PLATE 46

THE HEART OF THE WHIRLPOOL, M51

The Whirlpool Galaxy is a large spiral galaxy 23 million light years away. This image is a close-up of the galaxy's core. Right in the heart of the galaxy is a bright ball of stars about 80 light years across which is brighter than a hundred million Suns. These stars are so close together that it is easier to measure them in astronomical units – as used to measure distances in our Solar System – than light years. They were probably formed when a small companion galaxy passed close to the core about 400 million years ago, stirring up gas and causing it to collapse into protostars.

Around this region is an area of old stars, probably some 8 billion years old, which is 1500 light years in diameter. Even farther out is another band of younger stars, less than 10 million years old as we see them. The formation of these young stars was probably triggered by a shock wave emanating from the active central regions.

Right at the very centre of this image, near the dark dust lanes, is a mass of stars less than 5 light years in diameter with a luminosity of over a million Suns.

See glossary entries: astronomical unit; light year; spiral galaxy

PLATE 47

AN ACTIVE GALAXY, NGC 7742

Many galaxies are active in unusual ways. In visible light this galaxy looks like an ordinary but small spiral. In fact, NGC 7742 is one of a class of spiral galaxies known as Seyfert galaxies. These galaxies have unusually bright cores, and the stars and gas in their central regions seem to be moving much faster than in normal spiral galaxies. The ring of white around the core of NGC 7742, which gives this galaxy the appearance of an egg, is a region of star formation about 3000 light years from the core. The rest of the galaxy can be seen as a faint blur around the edges of the 'white'.

These galaxies are named after Carl Seyfert, who first drew attention to them in 1943. His spectroscopic studies of these objects showed clear evidence of hot clouds of gas moving at tremendous speeds, sometimes thousands of kilometres per second. At the time, this was astonishing evidence of violent activity going on in the Universe. About one-tenth of all large spiral galaxies are seen to be active in this way. This probably means that all such galaxies (including our Milky Way) spend about a tenth of their lives as Seyferts, perhaps in repeated short bursts of activity.

Some other apparently normal galaxies are expelling from their cores huge jets of material that are visible only at radio wavelengths. Still others show evidence of very-high-energy processes going on in their cores, and particles moving at very nearly the speed of light. Something very extreme is happening at the centres of many galaxies.

See glossary entries: light year; Milky Way; Seyfert galaxy; spiral galaxy

PLATE 48

A CENTRAL BLACK HOLE

It has been thought for several years that the only objects in the Universe capable of producing many of the effects seen in active and unusual galaxies are enormous black holes at their centres.

Black holes are objects that gravity has crushed down to a single point. The gravitational pull of a black hole is so great that even light cannot escape if it passes too close to the black hole and is trapped. The only way we can detect a black hole is indirectly. As material flows into the black hole, caught in its gravitational grip, it heats up, getting hotter and denser as it moves closer to the black hole. As it heats up, the material produces highly energetic radiation, which can escape as it has not yet passed the limiting point beyond which everything is trapped. It is this light that we are able to see.

This is an image of the centre of the elliptical galaxy NGC 6251, 300 million light years away. The bright central spot is the region around the black hole, bright from the hot material it is about to swallow. The dark patch is a disk of material which is being sucked onto the black hole but which is not yet hot enough to radiate strongly and become visible.

See glossary entries: black hole; elliptical galaxy; light year

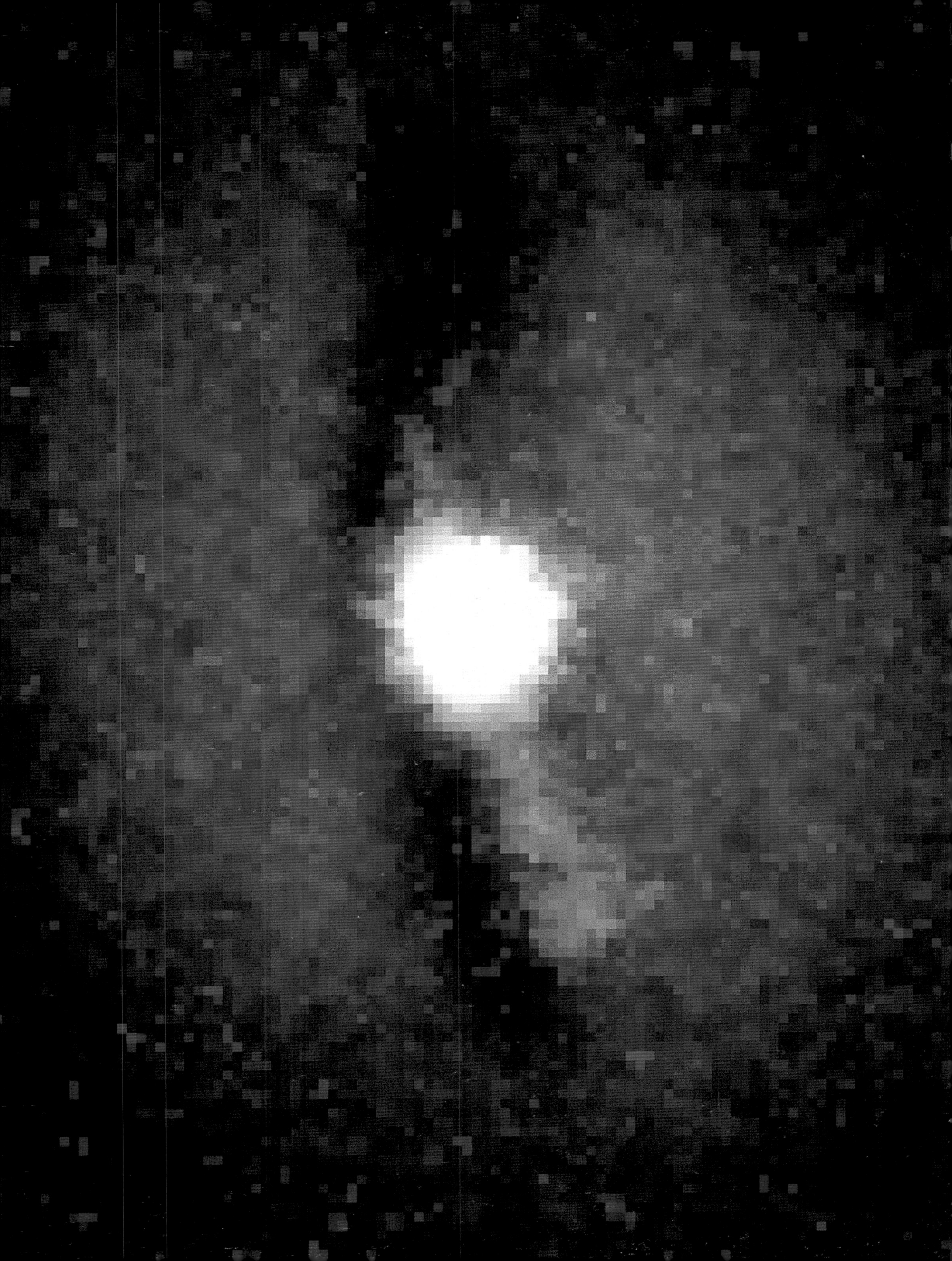

PLATE 49

MASSIVE BLACK HOLE IN GALAXY NGC 7052

At the centre of the galaxy NGC 7052 is a 3700 light year diameter disk of gas and dust which is spiralling onto a huge black hole weighing 300 million times as much as the Sun. Invisible in this picture are two jets of electrons spurting out from each pole of the black hole, accelerated nearly to the speed of light by the strong magnetic field around the black hole.

The disk around the black hole contains 3 million Suns' worth of material, and is thought to be the remains of a satellite galaxy which merged with NGC 7052. What suggests this is the fact that the disk and the jets are not perpendicular, which means that the black hole and the disk could not have formed together.

It now seems likely that most galaxies contain a massive black hole such as this. There is good evidence that the Milky Way has a fairly large black hole at its centre, as do many of our neighbouring galaxies, even though they are not active. Perhaps galaxies become active only when they undergo a merger or an interaction with another galaxy which perturbs them, pushing material onto the black hole.

See glossary entries: black hole; galaxy; light year; Milky Way

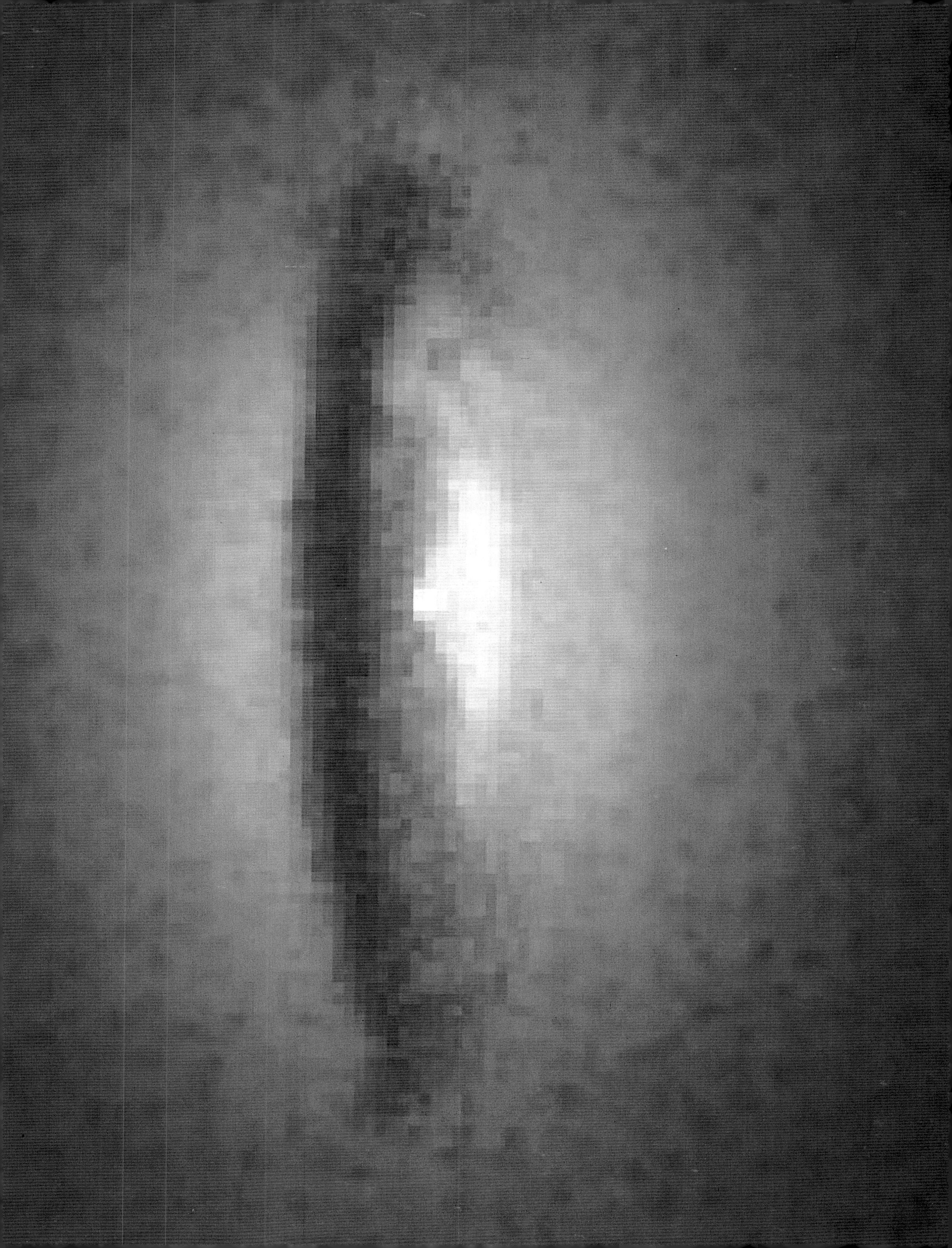

PLATE 50

JETS FROM A BLACK HOLE IN GALAXY NGC 4151

At the centre of the galaxy NGC 4151 is thought to be yet another supermassive black hole. This image of the core of NGC 4151, taken in visible light with WF/PC-2, shows two jets of material being shot out from the poles of the black hole at high speed.

Around a black hole, all of the hot material falling into it creates strong magnetic fields. Particles can be accelerated in these magnetic fields along trajectories leading out from the poles of the black holes, reaching near light speeds in a very short time.

Jets such as these can extend for millions of light years beyond the galaxy itself. At such large distances they can be seen quite clearly with radio telescopes as they smash into the gas that lies between galaxies. This image, however, shows the very heart of the galaxy where the jets are being formed.

NGC 4151 is an active Seyfert galaxy, like NGC 7742 (Plate 47).

See glossary entries: black hole; light year; Seyfert galaxy; WF/PC

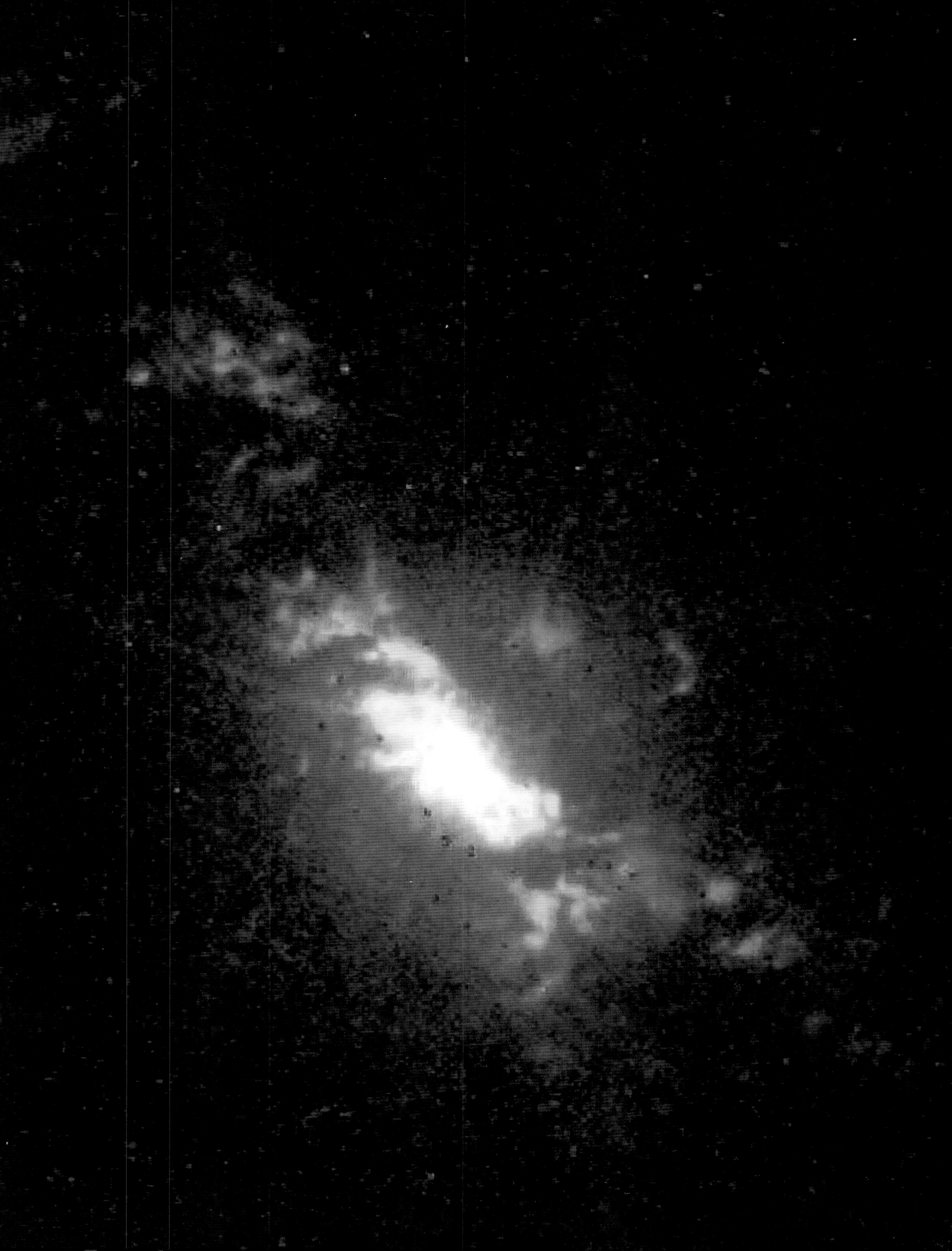

PLATE 51

JETS AT THE HEART OF GALAXY NGC 4151

This is another image of the heart of NGC 4151 (Plate 50), this time looking specifically at the oxygen in the gas around the black hole. The large line across the centre is created by the black hole itself, but the jets can be seen clearly on either side.

The instrument that took this image, the Space Telescope Imaging Spectrometer, or STIS, is capable of imaging an object while also obtaining a spectrum at the same time. This image is in visual light, but STIS can also do the same in ultraviolet light.

The ability of the Hubble Space Telescope to look at objects at a variety of different wavelengths allows far more information to be gathered than from a typical telescope on the ground, where the intervening atmosphere makes observing in the infrared difficult and in the ultraviolet impossible. Data from the HST can be combined with information collected in many other wavelength ranges to gain a picture of the object across most of the spectrum. Other satellites observe in high-energy X-rays and gamma-rays, and telescopes on the ground observe in long-wavelength radio and microwaves.

See glossary entries: black hole; gamma-rays; STIS; ultraviolet light

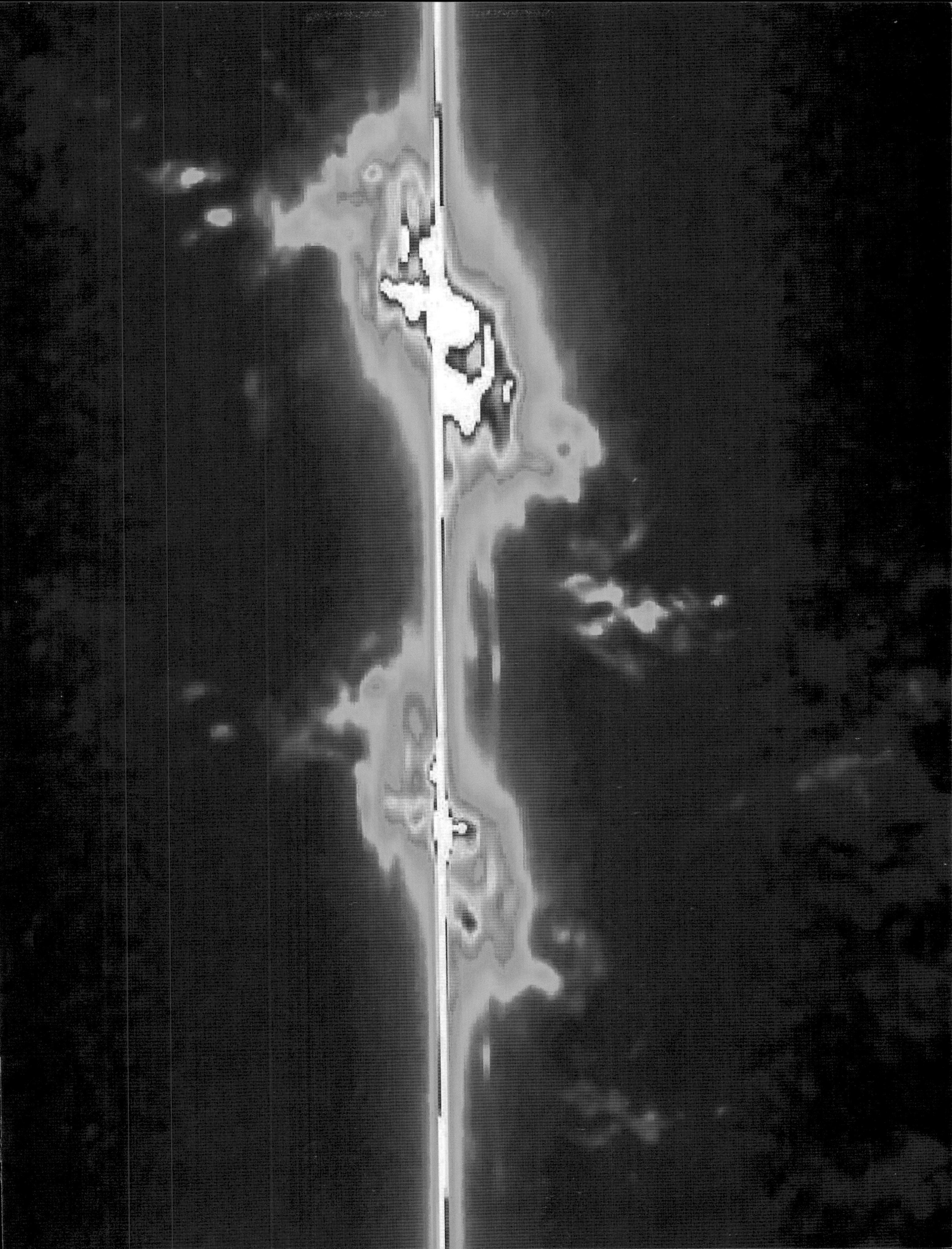

PLATE 52

THE SIGNATURE OF A BLACK HOLE

This picture shows the spectrum of light from the centre of the active galaxy M84. Light, like sound, can have a Doppler effect. The sound from a siren approaching you will have a shorter wavelength (as the sound 'catches up' with itself) than when the siren is moving away, when the wavelength is longer. With light, something moving away looks redder (longer wavelength) than when moving towards you, when it looks bluer (shorter wavelength). This is known as the redshift (or blueshift) of light.

This shifting of wavelengths allows the speed (in the direction towards or away from you) of a star or gas which emits light to be determined with incredible accuracy. Astronomers often measure redshifts and blueshifts in terms of velocity. This spectrum of the core of M84 shows shifts of 1.4 million km/h. This means that material on either side of the centre is moving towards or away from us at this speed, which is therefore the orbital speed of the material around the central black hole. The shifts are very obvious in this spectrum.

Knowing how gravity works (even in extreme conditions like this) allows us to work out the mass of the object at the centre around which the material is orbiting. In this case there is an object less than 27 light years across weighing 300 million times more than the Sun. If it is not a black hole, then it must be something even stranger, and as yet unknown to science.

See glossary entries: black hole; blueshift; Doppler effect; light year; redshift

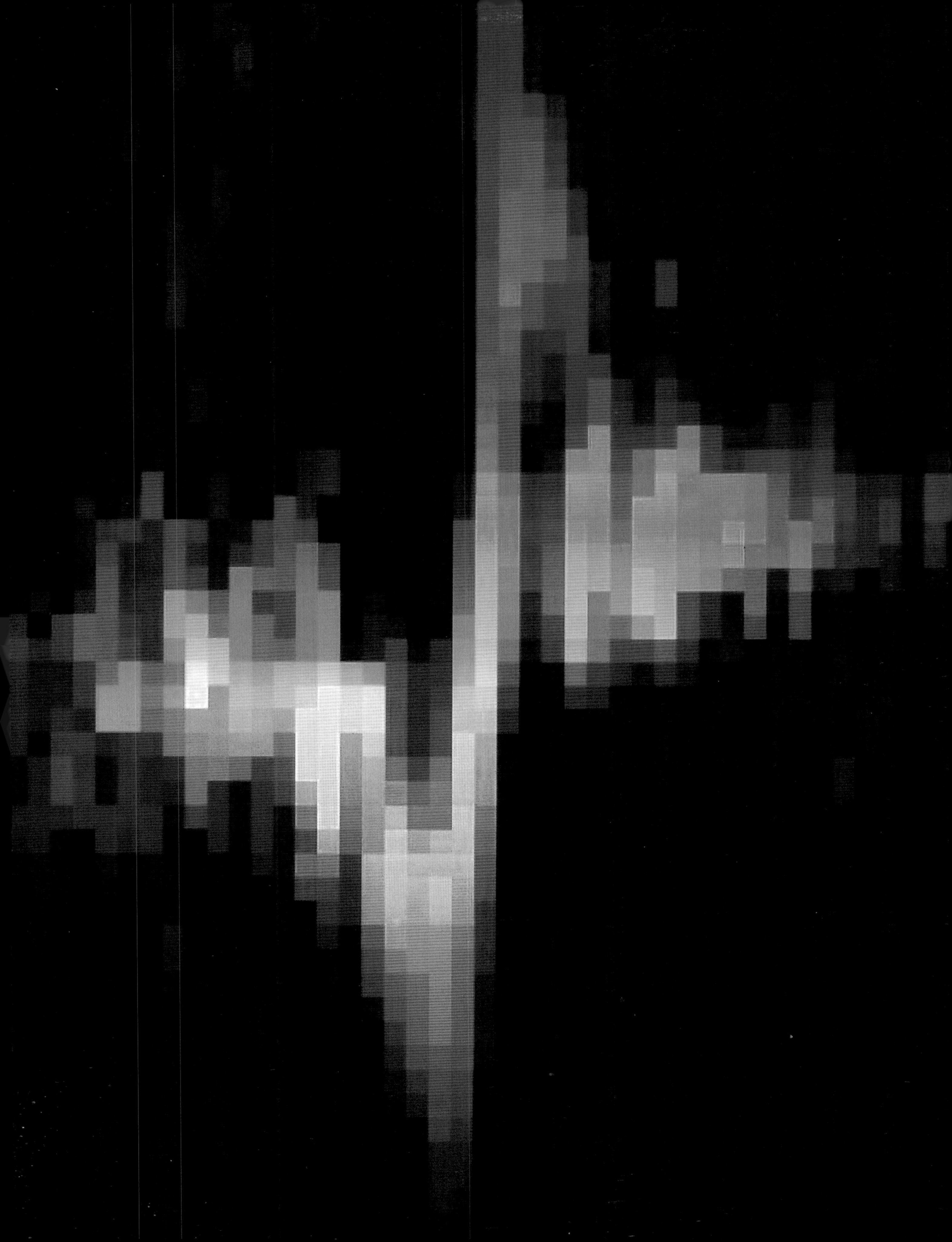

PLATE 53

HUBBLE DEEP FIELD SOUTH

This is one of the deepest views of the Universe ever obtained. Together with the original Hubble Deep Field (Plate 37), this image was obtained as part of a project to view galaxies as far away as possible. A region of the southern sky in the constellation Tucana was selected, and all the Hubble Space Telescope's instruments were trained for a long time on this relatively empty part of the sky (empty of stars, that is).

The HST probed the Hubble Deep Field South at visible and infrared wavelengths to observe galaxies as they were long ago. Light takes a year of time to travel a distance of one light year, so we see the nearest star, 4 light years away, as it was four years ago. All the galaxies in this picture are at least millions of light years distant, and some of the farthest galaxies are billions of light years away. Thus we are able to see some distant galaxies as they were so long ago that they were still in the process of forming.

See glossary entries: galaxy; infrared light; light year; look-back time

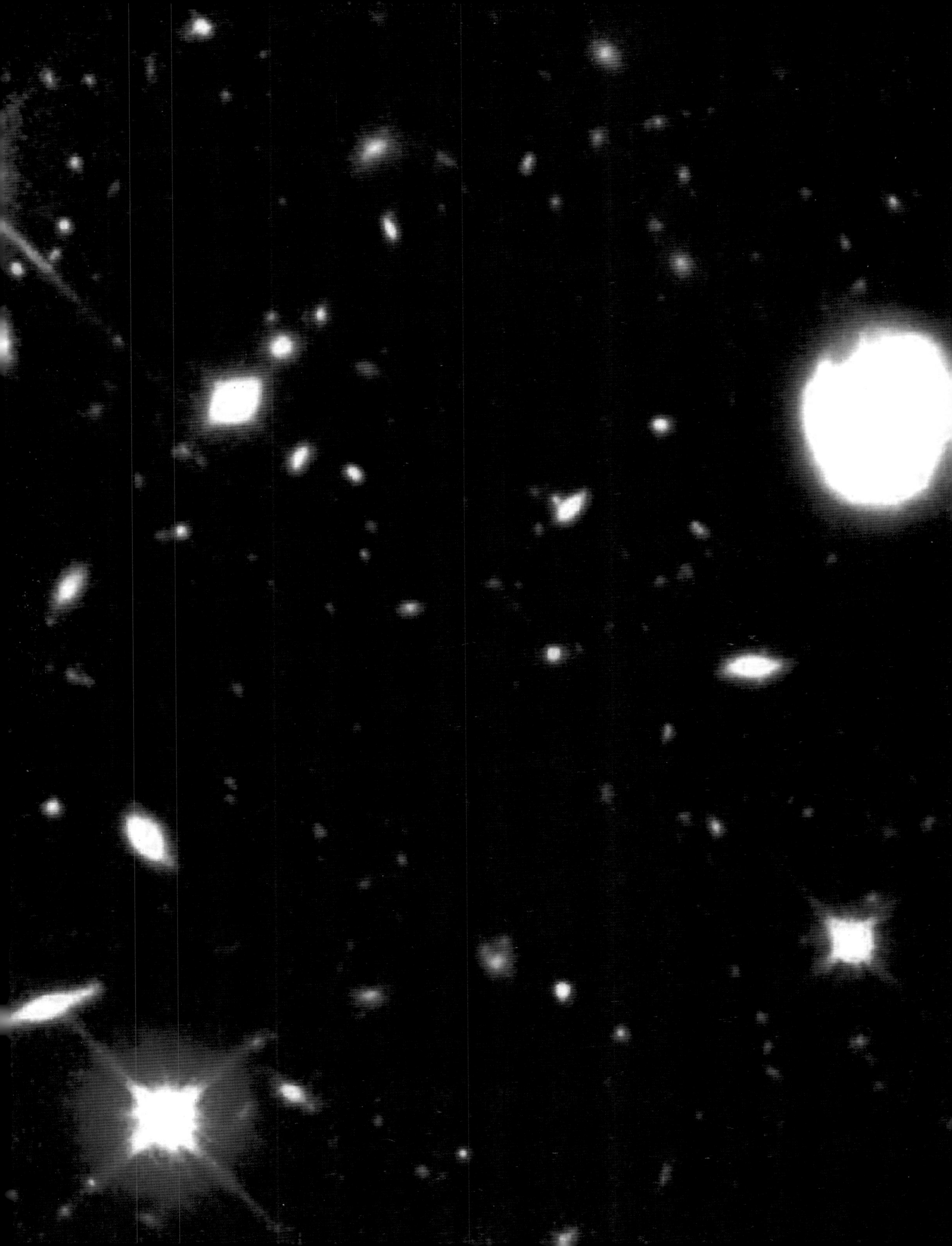

PLATE 54

QUASAR IRAS 04505–2958

Quasars are the intrinsically brightest objects we have yet discovered. At first their nature was unknown. They appeared as points of light, but in their spectra they were unlike any star. The name quasar comes from a contraction of 'quasi-stellar object', because they look like stars but they are not stars.

In the spectra of quasars, where we would expect to see spectral lines of visible light we see instead spectral lines of ultraviolet light. This extreme redshift of the quasars' ultraviolet light can have been caused only by the expansion of the Universe, so quasars must be extremely distant objects. Their brightness and distance make quasars more luminous than a thousand normal galaxies.

The Hubble Space Telescope has allowed us to image quasars in remarkable detail, showing that the source of their light is a tiny region only a few tens of light years across in the centre of a 'host' galaxy. This source has to be a supermassive black hole like those seen in nearby galaxies (e.g. Plates 47, 48, 49, 50 and 51). Quasars are therefore just an extreme version of these active galaxies, fuelled by material falling onto a massive black hole.

The quasar shown here, IRAS 04505–2958, lies 3 billion light years away and is sitting in a galaxy that is undergoing a collision with another galaxy. This collision is presumably forcing material down onto the central black hole, releasing the energy that we see.

See glossary entries: black hole; light year; quasar; redshift; ultraviolet light

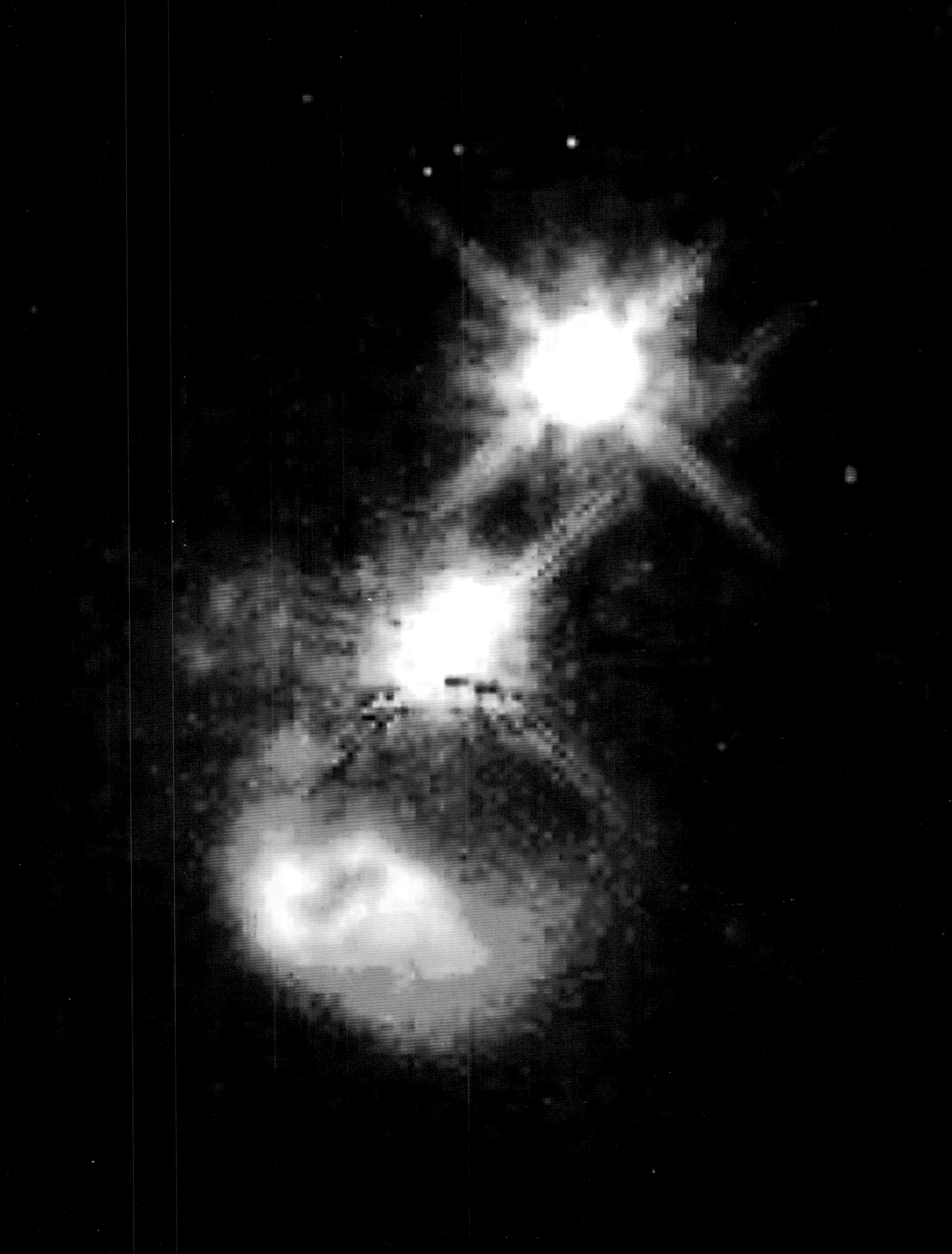

PLATE 55

THE HOST OF QUASAR PG 0052+251

The most surprising thing that was discovered when the Hubble Space Telescope imaged the host galaxies of quasars is that some of them, like PG 0052+251 here, seem to be perfectly normal. It was assumed that galaxy mergers or collisions were required to disturb the tremendous amounts of material needed to fuel the central black hole and produce quasar activity. Such mergers are expected to have been much more common in the early stages of the evolution of galaxies, as galaxies grew by accreting smaller ones.

Quasars produce around 1000 billion times as much energy as the Sun, which means that an amount of material equal to the mass of the Sun must be consumed by the black hole each year. It is still a mystery how a normal spiral galaxy like PG 0052+251 can contribute this amount of infall. Even if a normal host galaxy could somehow fuel a quasar, it is hard to see how it can remain normal, given the huge amount of radiation produced by the quasar.

The explanation might be that the dynamics of the stars and gas in the centre of the galaxy is being affected by a halo of dark matter (it must be dark because we cannot see it) surrounding the galaxy. Their orbits may be being disturbed if the halo is not spherical or elliptical, causing them to move towards the centre of the galaxy.

See glossary entries: black hole; quasar; spiral galaxy; Sun

PLATE 56

A GRAVITATIONAL LENS

Gravitational lensing is a prediction of Einstein's general theory of relativity, which tells us that gravity bends light. The stronger the gravitational field, the greater the bending. This means that massive objects like stars or galaxies can act as lenses, focusing the light of an object behind them towards us if everything is aligned in the right way. Recently, many examples of gravitational lenses have been found.

In the simplest version of gravitational lensing, predicted by Einstein in the 1930s, you would have a single point mass (something like a star) exactly on the line between us and a distant object – perhaps a quasar. In those circumstances, the lensed image of the distant quasar would form a circle (known as an Einstein ring) around the foreground star. When the foreground object is not a point mass but is spread out (like a cluster of galaxies), Einstein's equations tell us that the most likely form of lensing will be to produce either two or four images of the distant object, because light has travelled by two or four different routes around the intervening object. But if the mass in the lensing system is distributed unevenly as well as being spread out, and it is not exactly on the line between us and the distant object, these images can be distorted and broken up to make multiple images along individual arcs, parts of the Einstein ring that would appear if the lens were perfect.

This picture shows light from the quasar PG 1115+080, 8 billion light years away, lensed by an elliptical galaxy 3 billion light years away. The elliptical galaxy is in the centre of the image, surrounded by a smear of light and three images of the quasar.

See glossary entries: elliptical galaxy; gravitational lens; quasar

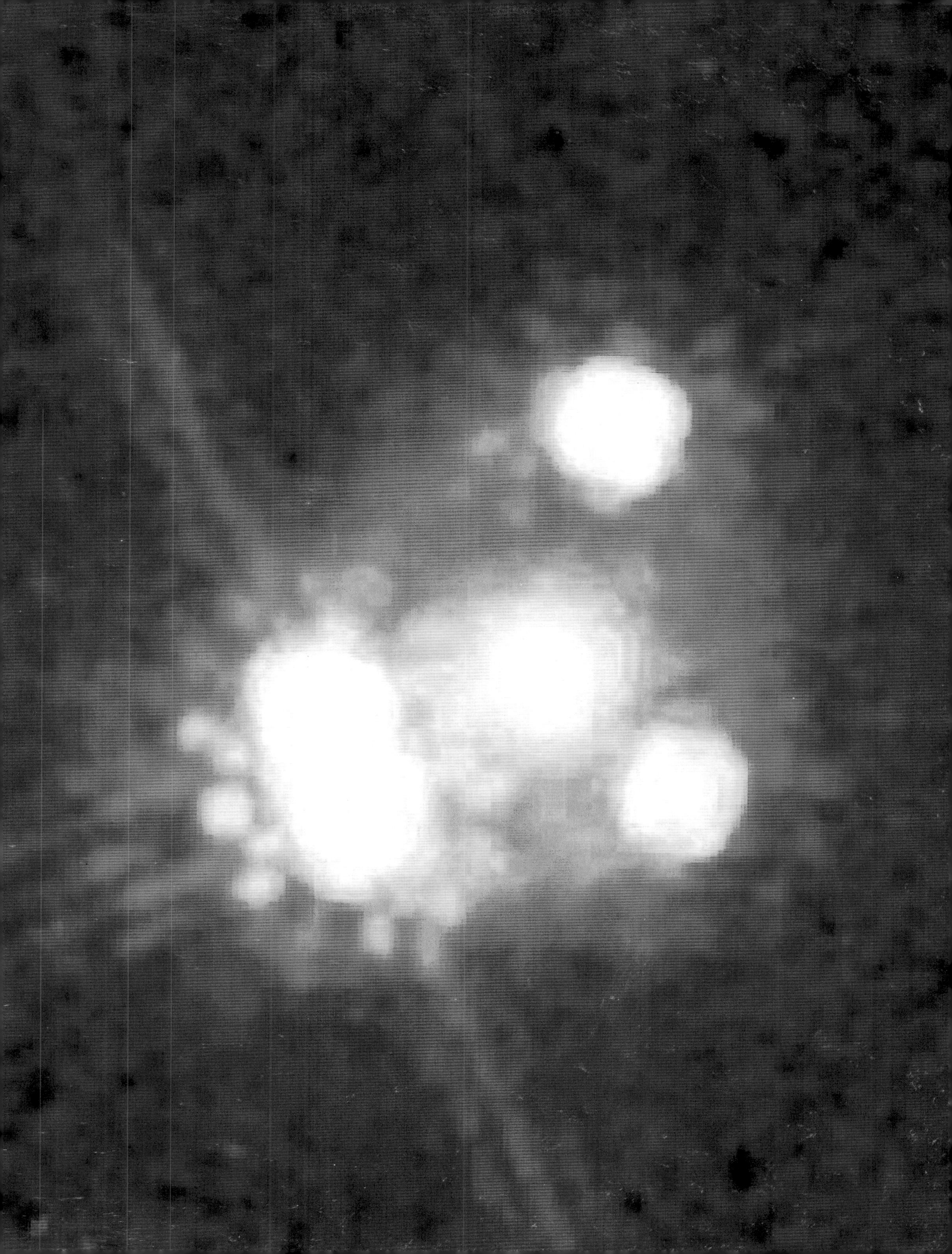

PLATE 57

LOOKING AT QUASAR PG 1115+080

In this image of the gravitational lens system shown in Plate 56, the image of the lensing foreground galaxy has been removed by computer processing. What is left is the gravitationally lensed quasar on its own.

The light from the quasar can be seen to be smeared out into a ring on which the three exceptionally bright sources were superimposed. This ring is a close approximation to an Einstein ring, the perfect circular image that would be created if the Earth, the lensing galaxy and the quasar were exactly aligned along the line of sight.

The ability to take images apart like this gives us information not only about the distant quasar, but also about how matter is distributed in the lens, enabling us to calculate the galaxy's mass.

See glossary entries: gravitational lens; quasar

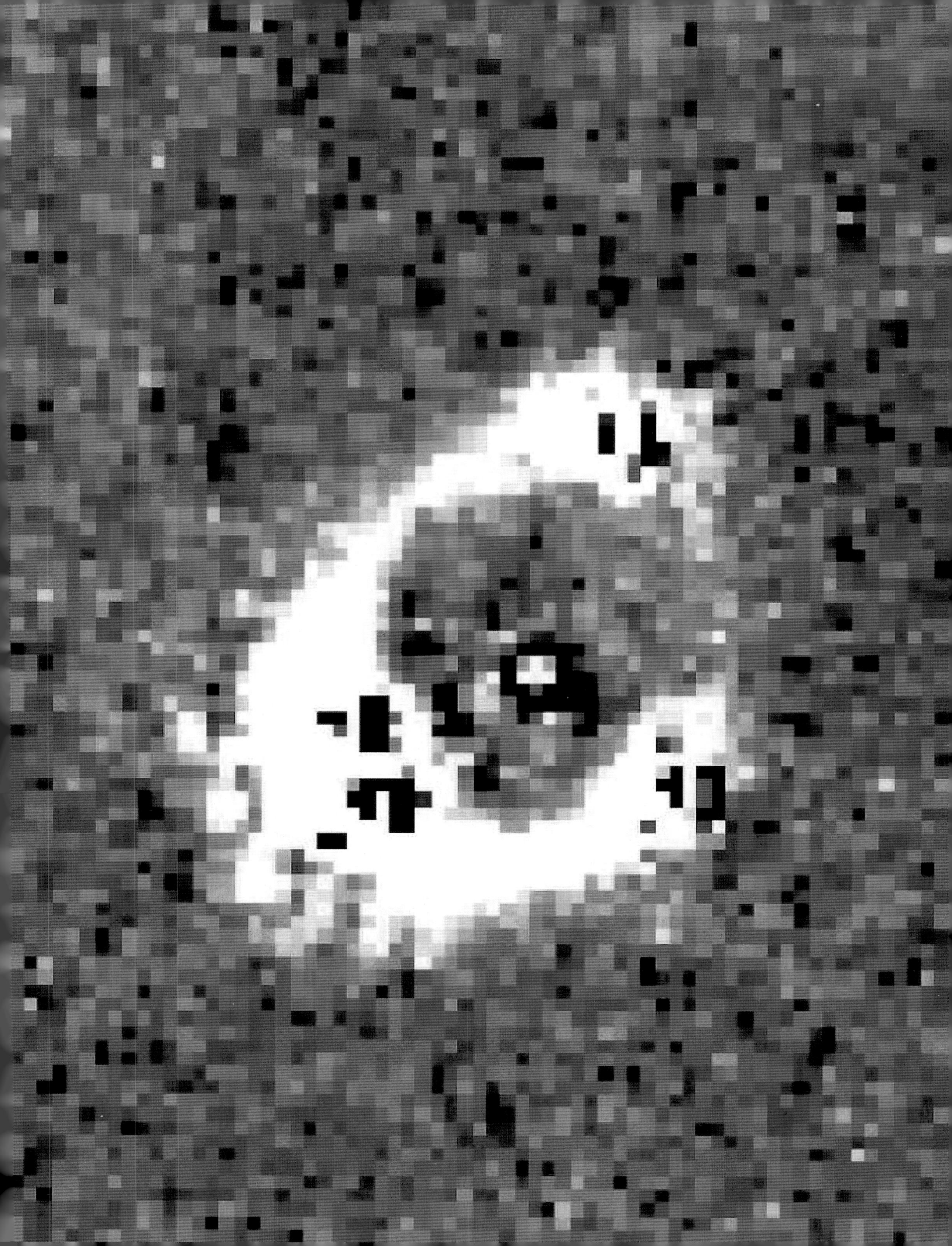

PLATE 58

THE MOST DISTANT GALAXY

This picture of a galaxy cluster contains an image of the most distant galaxy yet detected. The strange red smear at 5 o'clock is a gravitationally lensed image of this galaxy.

The lensing cluster, CL 1358+62, is 5 billion light years away and the galaxy behind it is an astonishing 13 billion light years away, a distance so great that the Universe was only 7 per cent of its present age when this light left the galaxy. We are therefore seeing it while it was still forming. When the image of this galaxy is processed electronically, several bright starburst regions hundreds of light years across are revealed, showing star formation proceeding at a far faster rate than in virtually all the other galaxies we see today.

CL 1358+62 is a fairly typical galaxy cluster. Right at the centre of this image can be seen a giant elliptical galaxy which resides in the core of CL 1358+62. Virtually all galaxy clusters contain a massive elliptical galaxy such as this. They probably form as galaxies fall into the centre of the cluster and merge. Many of these giant elliptical (or cD) galaxies are active galaxies containing massive black holes.

See glossary entries: black hole; elliptical galaxy; gravitational lens

PLATE 59

A GAMMA-RAY BURST

We finish with one of the most exciting and mysterious phenomena in the Universe. Short bursts of extremely intense gamma radiation are recorded by detectors on orbiting satellites at the rate of a few each day, from seemingly random positions in the sky. Gamma-rays are the most energetic form of light, far more dangerous even than X-rays because of the amount of energy they carry. Luckily for us the Earth's atmosphere shields us from gamma radiation from space; but satellites are able to observe the sky in gamma radiation.

Until recently, no one had seen a gamma-ray burst in anything but gamma-rays. Gamma-ray satellites are not very good at pinpointing where in the sky an object is, because of the difficulty of observing such high-energy radiation. The best they can do is indicate the area where a gamma-ray burst happened, but this area is so large that it is full of sources of radiation at other wavelengths.

That was the case until GRB 970228, the 228th gamma-ray burst to be detected in 1997, for which the Hubble Space Telescope managed to find a counterpart in visible light. This showed that gamma-ray bursts originate in distant galaxies, and so must be the most energetic events in the Universe.

See glossary entries: gamma-rays; gamma-ray burster

PLATE 60

GRB 971214

Here is GRB 971214, detected on 28 February 1997. This image is a combination of WF/PC-2 images taken on 26 March and 7 April 1997. The arrow indicates the fireball of the explosion, and just below and to the right of it is the galaxy in which we think GRB 971214 occurred.

No one is quite sure what causes a gamma-ray burst. The best guess is that it happens when two neutron stars in orbit around each other merge. The neutron stars will spiral in towards each other, and when they finally collide they will create a black hole. Not all of the material in the neutron stars goes into making the black hole, however. Some of it is superheated to millions of degrees and blasted away from the merger at velocities close to that of light.

If a gamma-ray burst were to take place in our region of the Milky Way, its radiation would penetrate the Earth's atmosphere and cause tremendous damage to the biosphere. Some astronomers have speculated that events like this may have been behind some of the 'mass extinctions' of life on Earth during geological history. There is a suggestion, though (from observations of distant galaxies), that these events were more common when the Universe was younger. We do not see gamma-ray bursts in nearby (that is, old) galaxies. It may be that intelligent life could evolve in a galaxy like the Milky Way only after the bursts die down. If so, it may be that we are one of the most advanced forms of life in the entire Universe.

See glossary entries: black hole; gamma-rays; gamma-ray burster; Milky Way; neutron star; WF/PC

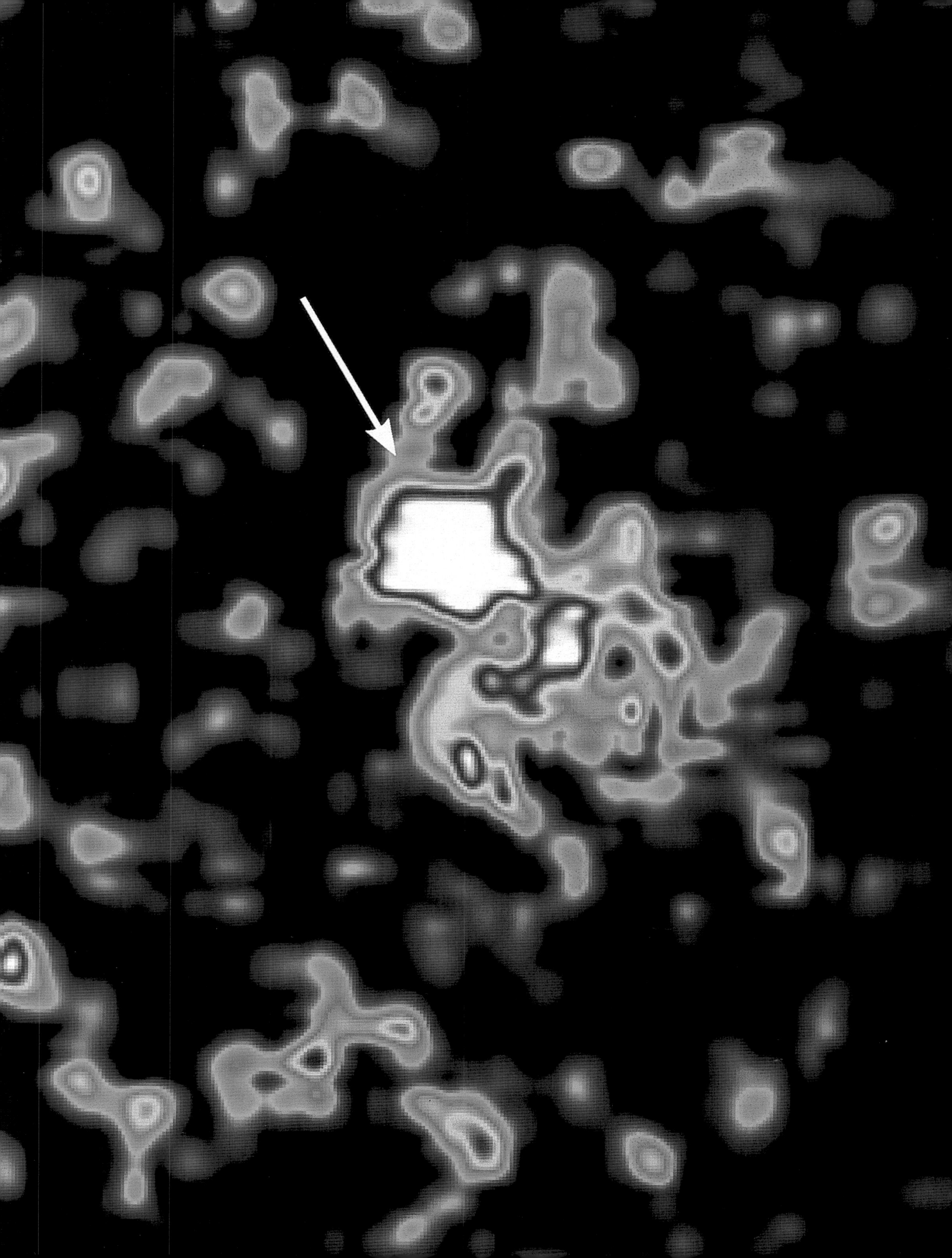

EXTENDED GLOSSARY

Note: within glossary entries, cross-references to terms which have their own glossary entries are in bold type.

age of the Universe The time that has elapsed since the Universe was created in the Big Bang. Ever since the Big Bang the Universe has been expanding, so to calculate its age it is necessary to know how fast the Universe is expanding today, and how much the expansion has slowed down since the Big Bang. Working out the expansion rate requires the distances to other galaxies, beyond the Milky Way. All but a few of our nearest galactic neighbours are receding from us, and from one another, as the Universe expands, and this shows up as a **redshift** in the light from these galaxies, which is relatively easy to measure. The distances are harder to measure, but once they are known the relationship between redshift and distance reveals how fast the Universe is expanding. To work out the age of the Universe then requires some theoretical input, using the equations of the general theory of relativity. But only certain **cosmological models**, as the resulting theoretical constructions are called, can be made to match the observations of the real Universe. In our own investigation of this problem, in collaboration with Martin Hendry, we have used distances to other galaxies based on observations of **Cepheid variable** stars obtained by the HST. This suggests that the age of the Universe is between 13 billion and 16 billion years. *See also* **distance scale of the Universe**.

arcsecond A measure of angle used in astronomy, indicating the size of objects as they appear on the sky. One arcsecond (or 1 second of arc) is a sixtieth of an arcminute, which is itself a sixtieth of a degree. There are 360 degrees in a circle. The size of the Moon on the sky, as viewed from Earth, is just over 30 arcminutes (half a degree). Many of the pictures in this book were obtained with the WF/PC camera on the HST, which can pick out details just a tenth of an arcsecond across. The farther away an object is, the larger the actual size of the feature this corresponds to.

astronomical unit (AU) A measure of distance and linear size used in astronomy. 1 AU is the average distance from the Earth to the Sun over the course of the year, and is roughly 150 million kilometres. This is a convenient yardstick to use in measuring distances within the Solar System, and is also the basis for a distance unit used in measuring distances to other stars, and even other galaxies. A hypothetical object that is 1 AU across is defined as being at a distance of 1 parsec (a contraction of the term 'parallax second of arc') if it subtends an angle of 1 arcsecond on the sky. Conversely, from a distance of 1 parsec (1 pc), the radius of the Earth's orbit would subtend an angle of 1 arcsecond. A parsec is just over

3.2616 **light years**. Our Milky Way Galaxy is about 28 000 parsecs (28 kiloparsecs) across, which is equivalent to about 90 thousand light years. Distances to other galaxies are measured in millions of parsecs (megaparsecs, or Mpc).

binary system Two stars in orbit around each other. The majority of stars are members of binaries, or more complicated star systems.

black dwarf An old star which has used up all of its supply of nuclear fuel, collapsed into a ball about the same size as the Earth, and cooled so much that it no longer emits any light. *See also* **white dwarf**.

black hole A concentration of matter which has such a strong gravitational pull that nothing, not even light, can escape from it. The popular image of a black hole is of a star several times more massive than our Sun, which has collapsed at the end of its life to make a hole in space a few kilometres across. Such black holes do exist, and are detected when they are in orbit around an ordinary star. The black hole sucks matter off the visible star, and in the process of swallowing it generates X-rays and radio noise which we can detect. But it is also possible for a black hole to be made up of a concentration of mass equivalent to a million Suns or more, spread out over a volume the diameter of our Solar System, at the centre of a galaxy. As they swallow matter from the surrounding galaxy, these objects also generate radio noise and X-rays, as well as visible light. In 1994, the HST revealed hot material orbiting at speeds close to 1 per cent of the speed of light around just such a supermassive black hole at the heart of the galaxy M87. The mass of this particular black hole is close to three billion times the mass of our Sun.

blueshift A shift of features in the spectrum of light towards the blue (short-wavelength) end of the spectrum. A blueshift is usually caused by motion of the object emitting the light towards the observer. *See also* **redshift**.

brown dwarf An object intermediate in size between a planet and a star. Planets never generate enough heat in their interiors to shine by their own light. Stars form from the collapse of a cloud of gas and dust in space, as it shrinks under its own weight. Such collapsing clouds get hot enough inside to start shining simply because gravitational energy is released as they collapse. If they get hot enough, this starts nuclear reactions which keep the stars shining. But a brown dwarf never gets hot enough inside to trigger nuclear reactions, although it may glow for a while as a dim, red object. This happens if the mass of the object is less than about 8 per cent of the mass of our Sun. For comparison, the mass of Jupiter, the largest planet in the Solar System, is 0.1 per cent of the mass of our Sun.

catalogue A list of interesting astronomical objects, with data on their positions and other properties. The two most relevant to the present book are the Messier Catalogue, which lists 103 bright clusters and nebulae observed by the French astronomer Charles

Messier in the second half of the 18th century, and the New General Catalogue of Nebulae and Clusters of Stars, abbreviated to NGC, which was first published in 1888 and later extended to inclue more than 13 000 entries. (Many of the 'nebulae' are in fact galaxies, which the compilers of the catalogues had no way of knowing.) Some objects appear in both catalogues – the Andromeda Galaxy, for example, is known both as M31 and as NGC 224.

CCD *See* **charge coupled device**.

Cepheid variable A bright star which changes in brightness in a very regular, periodic way. These stars are of key importance in determining astronomical distances, because it turns out that the exact period of such a star (the time it takes to brighten, fade, then brighten again) depends on its average brightness. So by measuring the period of a Cepheid, astronomers can calculate its intrinsic brightness. Then, by comparing this value with how faint the star looks on the sky, they can work out how far away it is. This technique yields direct measurements of the distances to a few dozen nearby galaxies, the first step in establishing the **distance scale of the Universe**.

charge coupled device (CCD) Most astronomical 'photographs', including all the images from the HST, are nowadays obtained electronically using charge coupled devices. These are typically very small electronic detectors – perhaps a few centimetres square – made up of millions of individual sensors called picture elements, or pixels. Each pixel responds to **photons** of light falling on to it, producing an electronic signal which is processed digitally by a computer to create an image for printing or display on a TV screen, or for further processing inside the computer. A typical CCD may be made up of 2048 rows of pixels on each side, and each pixel carries 2 bytes of information, so just over 8 Megabytes of computer memory is needed to store an original image in its unprocessed form. The WF/PC on board the HST uses smaller CCDs, but a Wide Field Camera planned for installation on the next servicing mission will have an even bigger CCD array.

cosmological model Cosmologists cannot make models of the Universe out of papier mâché or balsa wood, so they have to describe it in terms of equations manipulated with the aid of computers. These computer models describe how different kinds of imaginary universe would behave – for example, how fast they would expand. By comparing observations of the real Universe today with these simulations, cosmologists can find which models best describe the real Universe. These particular models can then be used to give us an idea of how the Universe was born and how it will age.

cluster Either a group of stars within a galaxy (*see* **globular cluster**), or a group of galaxies in the Universe at large.

disk galaxy A galaxy similar to our own Milky Way, with a disk of stars typically about 100 000 light years across and perhaps 10 000 light years thick, and a central bulge of stars, looking overall rather like a fried egg. A disk galaxy like the Milky Way contains several hundred billion stars like the Sun. *See also* **galaxy**.

distance scale of the Universe One of the most important discoveries in the whole of science, not just astronomy, is that the Universe is expanding, with galaxies retreating from one another. The rate at which other galaxies are seen to be receding from any galaxy you choose to measure the expansion from is proportional to their distance from the chosen galaxy. Because the recession velocity is easily measured from the cosmological **redshift**, this means that if the constant of proportionality in the relationship 'redshift is proportional to distance' can be worked out from measurements of nearby galaxies whose distances are known from other studies (for example, using **Cepheid variable** stars), then distances to all galaxies with known redshifts can be inferred. This defines the distance scale of the Universe. The constant is known as **Hubble's constant**, or the Hubble parameter, and it has a value between 50 and 80 kilometres per second per megaparsec (see **parsec**). If we say, for the sake of argument, that the numerical value of the constant is 50, that means that a galaxy with a redshift of 50 km/s is 1 Mpc away, a galaxy with a redshift of 100 km/s is 2 Mpc away, and so on. If the value of the constant is really 80, the distance scale is correspondingly smaller, and the inferred distances to all galaxies are only five-eighths as large.

Doppler effect An effect on the light from a moving object which changes the wavelength of features in the spectrum of the light. If the object is moving towards us, we see a **blueshift** in the light; if it is moving away from us, we see a **redshift**. The size of the shift tells us how fast the object is moving through space. Sound can also suffer a Doppler effect, which, for example, changes the note of the siren on a fast-moving vehicle, such as a police car.

dwarf galaxy A small galaxy which contains only a few million stars, compared with the several hundred billion stars in the Milky Way. *See also* **galaxy**.

elliptical galaxy A system of stars, shaped like a convex lens, which may look elliptical or circular on the sky, depending on its orientation. The masses of elliptical galaxies range from a few million times the mass of the Sun to about a thousand billion times the mass of the Sun. *See also* **galaxy**.

galaxy A collection of stars, held together by gravity, forming an island in space. The smallest dwarf galaxies contain only a few million stars. The largest galaxies, giant ellipticals, contain thousands of billions of stars and may be more than a hundred kiloparsecs across. They get their name from their smooth shape, rather like an American football, although many elliptical galaxies are almost spherical. All the stars we can see in the sky with our unaided eyes form part of a single galaxy, the Milky Way, which belongs to a different family, known as disk galaxies or spirals. These contain hundreds of millions of stars spread in a relatively thin disk (hence the name) with a central bulge of stars. The relative proportions of the disk and bulge are very similar to those of the white and yolk of a fried egg. An average disk galaxy like the Milky Way may be 30 kiloparsecs in diameter. The alternative name for disk galaxies, spirals, is given to them because many of those which we view face-on show a beautiful spiral pattern of bright stars, rather like the pattern made by cream as it is stirred into coffee. But not all disk galaxies have spiral features, so the generic name disk galaxy is preferred. Galaxies are associated with one another in groups called clusters, held together by gravity. A cluster may contain representatives of all the different kinds of galaxy, and may be made up of anything from a few dozen to a few thousand individual galaxies. It is actually the clusters of galaxies, rather than individual galaxies, that are moving away from one another as the Universe expands (*see* **distance scale of the Universe**). The term Galaxy, with a capital 'G', is reserved for our own Milky Way; 'galaxy' means any other galaxy, beyond the Milky Way.

gamma-rays Electromagnetic radiation, like light, but with much shorter wavelengths, in the range from one-tenth of a billionth of a metre to one hundred-thousandth of a billionth of a metre. The energies of gamma-rays are correspondingly higher than those of ordinary light.

gamma-ray burster An object which produces an intense but short-lived burst of gamma-rays. Until very recently, astronomers had no way of telling whether these events (detected by instruments on board satellites orbiting the Earth) were relatively modest explosions happening in our own Galaxy (comparable to supernova explosions), or much bigger explosions happening far away across the Universe. But in 1997 the HST produced an image of the fireball associated with a gamma-ray burst in a distant galaxy (*see* Plates 59 and 60). This shows that the bursts are enormously energetic, probably the most energetic phenomena that have happened in the Universe since the Big Bang itself. It is possible that they occur when two neutron stars collide, or when a neutron star collides with a black hole.

giant molecular cloud A large cloud of (mainly hydrogen) gas in a galaxy like our Milky Way. Discovered in the 1970s, using radio astronomy, these clouds contain millions of times as much mass as our Sun. They are the material from which new stars are made. One giant molecular cloud may contain several dense cores, each containing a thousand times as much mass as our Sun, with stars beginning to form inside them. The best-known giant molecular cloud is associated with the star-forming activity of the Orion Nebula.

globular cluster A densely packed ball of stars associated with a galaxy such as our own Milky Way. A globular cluster may contain thousands or millions of individual stars, and there are about 150 such clusters surrounding our Galaxy. In our part of the Galaxy, stars are sparsely distributed, and there is no other star within 1 parsec of the Sun. But at the heart of a globular cluster there may be a thousand stars in a single cubic parsec of space. Globular clusters resemble dwarf galaxies, and are thought to be very old systems which formed before the Milky Way itself.

gravitational lens A concentration of mass such as a galaxy or cluster of galaxies whose gravity bends light going past it and focuses it to produce one or (usually) several images of an object which is behind the concentration of mass. Although the images that are produced in this way are often distorted, the magnifying effect of the lens makes it possible to see faint objects that would otherwise be far beyond the range of our telescopes.

HI region (pronounced 'H-one region') A cold cloud of hydrogen gas in space, mostly in the form of electrically neutral atoms, with some diatomic molecules (H_2). A typical HI region is about 5 parsecs across and contains about 50 times as much mass as our Sun. HI regions do not radiate visible light, but are detected by the characteristic radio noise they emit at a wavelength of 21 centimetres.

HII region (pronounced 'H-two region') A cloud of hot hydrogen in space, which has been heated by the energy radiated from young stars embedded in it. This energy has knocked negatively charged electrons free from the original hydrogen atoms, leaving them as positively charged ions. A typical HII region is about 200 parsecs across, and the material radiates not only visible light but also infrared and ultraviolet radiation, producing spectacular images when viewed by instruments such as the WF/PC on the HST.

Hubble constant (Hubble parameter) *See* **distance scale of the Universe**.

infrared light Light which is made up of **photons** which each carry slightly less energy than those which make up red light. Infrared light lies just beyond the red end of the visible spectrum and is invisible to human eyes. However, it can still be recorded by instruments such as charge coupled devices.

kelvin A unit of temperature used by scientists. Zero on the Kelvin scale is the coldest temperature that can exist, and is, in round numbers, $-273°$ on the Celsius scale. Temperatures in kelvin are written without a degree sign, but each degree is the same size as a Celsius degree, so that 0°C becomes 273 K, and so on.

light year The distance covered by light, travelling at a speed of 299 792 458 metres per second, in one year. In round terms, this is 9500 billion kilometres, or 0.3 parsecs. A light year is a measure of distance, not of time (but *see* **look-back time**).

look-back time Because light travels at a finite speed, we always see things around us as they were in the past. The speed of light is so great (roughly 300 000 kilometres per second) that in everyday life this isn't noticeable. But the Sun is so far away that its light takes just over 8 minutes to reach the Earth, so we actually see the Sun as it was a little more than 8 minutes ago. Light from a star that is 10 light years away takes 10 years to reach us, so we see it as it was 10 years ago; and light from a galaxy a billion light years away has been a billion years on its journey – that galaxy has a look-back time of a billion years. This means that astronomers indulge in a form of time travel every time they train their telescopes on the sky, and the HST is a kind of time machine.

Messier number *See* **catalogue**.

Milky Way A disk galaxy containing several hundred billion stars, our home in space. The Sun is an ordinary star orbiting in the disk of the Milky Way, about two-thirds of the way out from the centre. *See also* **galaxy**.

molecular cloud A cloud of material between the stars in which most of the stuff in the cloud is gas, in the form of molecules. Small molecular clouds, perhaps a few light years across, are almost entirely made of very cold hydrogen gas. No stars form inside these small clouds of material, which may be a few light years across. **Giant molecular clouds**, which may be between 150 and 250 light years across, contain molecules of carbon monoxide and small quantities of other kinds of molecule, as well as the dominant hydrogen gas.

nebula Originally a name for any fuzzy patch of light on the sky. We now know that many of the objects originally called nebulae are other galaxies, beyond the Milky Way. These are still occasionally referred to by their old names – the Andromeda Galaxy, for example, is sometimes called the Andromeda Nebula. It is best to avoid this use of the term, though, since today 'nebula' is used for a cloud of gas and dust within our Milky Way galaxy. This may be a dark cloud of cold stuff silhouetted against a bright background, or it may be a brightly glowing cloud of hot material such as an **HII region**. Such nebulae are the birthplaces of stars. We also see such nebulae in other galaxies.

neutron star A compact stellar remnant in which about the same amount of matter as there is in the Sun has been squeezed into a ball of neutrons only a few kilometres across. *See also* **pulsar**, **supernova**.

NGC number *See* **catalogue**.

NICMOS The Near Infrared Camera and Multi-Object Spectrograph, an instrument installed on the HST during the first service mission. Because it is sensitive to 'light' from the infrared part of the spectrum, NICMOS is particularly good at penetrating dusty regions of space to see what lies behind the dust, and at imaging cool systems that do not glow brightly in visible light.

nova A relatively small stellar explosion (contrast with **supernova**) in which a faint star flares up into brief prominence. The name means 'new', because many novae are only visible to the naked eye during an outburst, so they were once thought to be literally new stars. A nova occurs when material from the surface of one star in a binary system spills over onto its neighbour, causing a brief flare of energetic activity. During such an outburst, a star increases in brightness by about a factor of 100 000, then fades away over a few weeks or months.

parsec A unit of distance used by astronomers, equal to 3.2616 **light years**. *See also* **astronomical unit**.

photon A particle of light. Light can be thought of as a stream of photons travelling across space, photons of a particular energy corresponding to light of a particular colour (or to radio waves, or X-rays, and so on). Sensitive astronomical instruments like those on the HST count the photons arriving from deep space one by one to build up images of objects far away across the Universe. *See also* **charge coupled device**.

planet Strictly speaking, any sizeable astronomical body which is in an independent orbit around a star, but is not a star itself and shines only because it reflects light from the parent star. The definition becomes a little vague at the lower end of the range of planetary masses – for example, there are more than a hundred thousand separate objects, each much smaller than the Earth, going round the Sun between the orbits of the planets Mars and Jupiter. These are the asteroids, sometimes called 'minor planets' because of their size. Everyone agrees that there are at least eight planets orbiting the Sun in our Solar System: Mercury, Venus, Earth, Mars, Jupiter, Saturn, Uranus and Neptune. Most textbooks say that there is a ninth planet, Pluto; but it has recently become clear that Pluto is simply the largest member of another family of minor planets orbiting farther out from the Sun, and therefore it is not a planet by the strict definition of the term. Similarly, a planet-sized object that has been ejected from its parent system (*see* Plate 36) is no longer really a planet, although it may be graced with that name. At the upper end of the mass scale of planets there is also scope for confusion, this time about where to draw the line between planets and the failed stars known as **brown dwarfs**; several of the objects in orbit around other stars which have made headline news as extrasolar 'planets' are, in fact, more likely to be brown dwarfs.

planetary nebula A nebula that looks something like a disk on the sky (without the HST's high resolution), and therefore resembles a planet in astronomical photographs. The name was coined by William Herschel in 1785, but we now know that planetary nebulae have nothing to do with planets. In reality, they are clouds of gas and some dust that have been blow away from a central star, which can often be seen using modern telescopes such as the HST. The name is sometimes extended to include nebulae that are produced in much the same way but do not look anything like planets – some are rings of material around the parent star, and others are shaped like a dumbbell, with double lobes. 'Classic' planetary nebulae are produced late in the life of a star, when it has swollen up to become a red giant. They have temperatures of around 12 000 K, contain about 20 per cent as much mass as our Sun, and move outward, away from the parent star, at speeds of about 20 km/s. They are made of star stuff, including heavier elements that have been manufactured from primordial hydrogen and helium, helping to provide the raw materials for later generations of stars, planets and possibly life forms. Some of the other nebulae which are included in the 'planetary' category are produced in more violent events which disrupt the outer layers of a star explosively.

pulsar A rapidly rotating **neutron star**, produced in the death throes of a massive star in a **supernova** explosion. Because the neutron star has a magnetic field, it beams radio energy out into the Universe as it rotates, like a celestial radio lighthouse. We detect the 'pulses' of radio noise which give pulsars their name when the beam of radiation flicks past our radio telescopes here on Earth.

quasar The violently energetic core of a young galaxy. The best explanation for the source of this energy is that a quasar consists of a black hole which contains about a hundred million times as much mass as our Sun, and which is swallowing material from the surrounding galaxy. As this matter is swallowed up, as much as half of its mass can be turned into energy, in line with Albert Einstein's famous equation $E = mc^2$. This is such an effective way to make energy that a quasar needs to swallow only as much mass as there is in a star like the Sun each year to keep shining. Older, nearby galaxies do not show quasar activity because the black holes in their hearts have swallowed up all the available matter in their central regions – but the black holes are still there. Because quasars are so bright, some of them are the most distant objects detectable by our telescopes, at more than 10 billion light years away.

red dwarf A very common kind of star, with a mass between about 20 per cent and 80 per cent of the mass of our Sun, which is cooler (and therefore redder in colour) than the Sun.

red giant A later stage in the life of stars like our Sun. The way energy is generated at the heart of a red giant by nuclear fusion reactions will raise the star's internal temperature, and this makes the outer part of the star swell up. Even though more energy is escaping from the swollen star, it is so big that less energy escapes across each square metre of its surface than escapes across each square metre of the surface of the Sun today. So its surface is actually cooler than that of the Sun, and looks red.

redshift A change in the spectrum of light from an object, which can be produced in any of three different ways (or by any combination of these processes operating together). It is detectable because each chemical element produces its own characteristic pattern of lines in the spectrum of light from a hot object such as a star. It is this pattern of lines that shifts bodily towards the red end of the spectrum when there is a redshift. One way in which this effect can arise is if the object emitting the light is moving away from you through space; this is known as the **Doppler effect** (similarly, a blueshift is seen in the spectrum of light from an object that is moving towards you). The Doppler effect is useful in astronomy because it enables us to measure the velocities of stars in our Galaxy. The second kind of redshift is caused by the expansion of the Universe. This is not a Doppler effect, because it is not caused by galaxies moving through space, but by the space between the galaxies stretching and affecting the light on its journey to us. This cosmological redshift shows that the Universe is expanding, and implies that it was born in a Big Bang. The third kind of redshift is caused by gravity. Photons escaping from the gravitational grip of an object lose energy as they struggle outwards, and red photons have less energy than blue photons, so the photons are redshifted. This gravitational redshift is tiny for a star like the Sun, but it has been measured in the light from some **white dwarf** stars. The most important of these effects for the purposes of the present book is the cosmological redshift. *See also* **distance scale of the Universe**.

Seyfert galaxy A kind of active galaxy in which about 1 per cent as much energy is released as in a typical quasar. The source of energy is probably matter falling into a moderately large black hole (about a million times the mass of the Sun) at the centre of a disk galaxy like the Milky Way.

spiral galaxy A **disk galaxy** with bright 'arms' of stars forming a spiral pattern. All spiral galaxies are disks, but not all disk galaxies are spirals. *See also* **galaxy**.

star A hot ball of gas, held together by gravity, which shines because nuclear reactions are releasing energy in its core. *See* **brown dwarf**, **red giant**, **Sun**, **white dwarf**.

STIS The Space Telescope Imaging Spectrometer, put in place during the first servicing mission in 1997. STIS is able to do two jobs at once, imaging an object and taking its spectrum at the same time. This gives information about the shape of an object as well as its composition.

Sun The Sun is an ordinary star. In one sense, it is almost exactly average, because it is in the middle of the range of stellar masses; in another sense it is slightly bigger than average, because there are many more smaller stars than there are larger stars. The Sun looks big and bright to us only because it is so close – a mere 150 million kilometres (that is, 1 **astronomical unit**, AU) away, compared with a distance of 1.3 parsecs (about 270 000 AU) to the next-nearest star. Stars generate heat in their interiors by the process of nuclear fusion, in which light chemical elements are converted into heavier ones. For most of a star's life, this involves the conversion of hydrogen into helium, and a star which generates its energy in this way is said to be a 'main sequence' star. The Sun is a main sequence star. It is about 5 billion years old, and has enough fuel to maintain itself in much the same state for another 5 billion years or so. When a main sequence star has used up all the available hydrogen in its core, it shrinks in the middle and gets hotter, which allows more complicated nuclear reactions to take place. In this phase of its life it will become a **red giant**. The Sun has a mass about 330 000 times greater than that of the Earth, and a radius 109 times bigger than the Earth's. Its surface temperature is a little under 6000 K, which gives it a yellow-orange colour – but the temperature at its heart, where hydrogen is being converted into helium, is about 15 million K.

supernova The violent death of a star at least eight times as massive as our Sun, releasing so much energy that it briefly shines as brightly as all the stars of the Milky Way put together – about a hundred billion times brighter than the Sun itself (but only 0.1 per cent as bright as a quasar). A supernova explosion happens because a star which has that much mass left over at the end of its life, when it has used up all the nuclear fuel that kept it shining as a star, cannot settle down quietly to become a white dwarf, but must collapse even further under its own weight, to become a neutron star or a black hole. This collapse releases huge amounts of gravitational energy, which drives a whole series of nuclear reactions that manufacture heavy elements (like uranium, lead and gold) and scatters them, along with the outer layers of the star, into interstellar space, where they help to provide the raw material for later generations of stars. The tiny residue of the massive star may become a black hole with a mass a few times that of our Sun, or a neutron star, in which about the mass of the Sun is squeezed into a sphere just 10 kilometres across. One cubic centimetre of neutron star stuff would weigh about 100 million tonnes, equivalent to squeezing all the human beings on planet Earth today into a thimble.

ultraviolet light Light made up of photons which each carry slightly more energy than photons of violet light, and which are invisible to human eyes, but can still be recorded by instruments such as **charge coupled devices**, and used to 'photograph' the source of the radiation.

WF/PC (pronounced 'wiffpick') The Wide Field/Planetary Camera, the instrument on board the HST which provided almost all the pictures in this book. The instrument actually contains three separate wide-field (wide-angle) cameras, and a smaller, more sensitive planetary camera with a narrower field of view. The cameras can be used independently, or between them the four CCDs can image a wide patch of sky simultaneously, producing a single picture. The three wide-angle cameras produce three square images which together make an L shape, like three bathroom tiles next to each other in a corner. The image from the CCD with the narrower field of view is placed in the corner of the L, like a smaller tile. The combined effect looks as if some of the images that are produced by adding the four pieces together have had bits cut out of one corner in a staircase shape. This is not a mistake in the printing – it is the way WF/PC views the Universe.

white dwarf The final stage in the life of a star like our Sun. During its time as a **red giant**, such a star loses about 20 per cent of its matter as it passes through a **planetary nebula** stage. Then, after all its nuclear fuel is exhausted, the remaining stellar cinder settles down into a cooling ball of star stuff, with the remainder of its mass contained in a sphere only about the same size as the Earth. The collapse of the star to make this compact ball makes it hot, as gravitational energy is released, so that it shines brightly with a white colour for a while; eventually, though, it will fade away and become a cold, dead black dwarf. One cubic centimetre of white dwarf material would weigh about a tonne – as much as a cubic metre of water.

LIST OF PLATES AND CREDITS

1. Launch of *Discovery*. CREDIT: NASA Johnson Space Center
2. The Hubble Space Telescope in orbit. CREDIT: NASA Johnson Space Center
3. Close-up of the Orion Nebula, M42. CREDIT: C R O'Dell, S K Wong (Rice University) and NASA
4. OMC-1: inside the Orion Molecular Cloud. CREDIT: E Erickson (ASETI Insitute/Ames Research Center) D Axon (STScI) and NASA
5. The Lagoon Nebula, M8. CREDIT: A Caulet (Space Telescope European Coordinating Facility, ESA) and NASA
6. The star Herschel 36. CREDIT: A Caulet (Space Telescope European Coordinating Facility, ESA) and NASA
7. A massive star and family in NGC 2264. CREDIT: R Thompson, M Rieke, G Schneider, S Stolovy (University of Arizona) and NASA
8. A bright star-forming region, NGC 2363. CREDIT: L Drissen, J-R Roy, C Robert (Département de Physique and Observatiore du Mont Megantic, Université Laval) and NASA
9. A giant star-forming region in M33. CREDIT: H Yang (University of Illinois), J Hester (University of Arizona) and NASA
10. Young star cluster. CREDIT: M Heydari-Malayeri (Paris Observatory, France), NASA and ESA
11. The massive star cluster NGC 1818. CREDIT: R Elson, R Sword (Cambridge, UK) and NASA. Original WF/PC-2 image courtesy of J Westphal, Caltech
12. Globular Cluster GC1 in Andromeda. CREDIT: M Rich, K Mighell, J Neill (Columbia University), W Freedman (Carnegie Observatories) and NASA
13. Imaging Betelgeuse. CREDIT: A Dupree (Harvard-Smithsonian Center for Astrophysics), R Gilliland (STScI), NASA and ESA
14. Separating Mira A and B. CREDIT: M Karovska (Harvard-Smithsonian Center for Astrophysics) and NASA
15. WR124: a violent Wolf–Rayet star. CREDIT: Y Grossdidier (University of Montreal and Observatoire de Strasbourg), A Moffat (University of Montreal), G Joncas (Université Laval), A Acker (Observatoire de Strasbourg) and NASA
16. The Pistol Star: the brightest star? CREDIT: D Figer (UCLA) and NASA
17. The centre of the Crab Nebula, M1. CREDIT: J Hester, P Scowern (Arizona State University) and NASA
18. Supernova 1987A in the Large Magellanic Cloud. CREDIT: Hubble Heritage Team (AURA/STScI/NASA)
19. The Ring Nebula, M57. CREDIT: Hubble Heritage Team (AURA/STScI) and NASA

20. Planetary nebula IC 3568. CREDIT: Howard Bond (Space Telescope Science Institute), Robin Ciardullo (Pennsylvania State University) and NASA
21. Planetary nebula NGC 5307. CREDIT: Howard Bond (Space Telescope Science Institute), Robin Ciardullo (Pennsylvania State University) and NASA
22. Planetary nebula NGC 7009. CREDIT: Bruce Balick and Jason Alexander (University of Washington), Arsen Hajan (US Naval Observatory), Yervant Terzian (Cornell University), Mario Perinotto (University of Florence, Italy), Patrizio Patriarchi (Arcetri Observatory, Italy) and NASA
23. The Stingray: the youngest planetary nebula. CREDIT: M Bobrowsky (Orbital Sciences Corporation) and NASA
24. The Egg Nebula. CREDIT: R Thompson, M Rieke, G Schneider, D Hines (University of Arizona), R Sahai (JPL), NICMOS Instrument Definition Team, and NASA
25. Planetary nebula NGC 7027. CREDIT: W Latter (SIRTF Science Center/Caltech) and NASA
26. A butterfly nebula. CREDIT: S Kwok (University of Calgary), R Rubin (NASA/Ames Research Center) and H Bond (STScI)
27. Turtle in space: NGC 6210. CREDIT: R Rubin and C Ortiz (NASA/Ames Research Center), P Harrington and N J Larne (University of Maryland), R Dufour (Rice University), and NASA
28. Cometary knots in the Helix Nebula, NGC 7923. CREDIT: C R O'Dell, K P Handron (Rice University) and NASA
29. The Bubble Nebula, NGC 7635. CREDIT: Hubble Heritage Team using data collected by J Hester (Arizona State University) and collaborators, and NASA
30. Nova T Pyxidis. CREDIT: M Shara, R Williams (STScI), R Gilmozzi (ESO) and NASA
31. Red dwarf Gliese 623b. CREDIT: C Barbieri (University of Padua), NASA and ESA
32. Gliese 105c: the smallest star? CREDIT: D Golimowski (JHU) and NASA
33. The disk of Beta Pictoris. CREDIT: A Schultz (CSC/STScI), S Heap (GFSC/NASA) and NASA
34. Young stellar disks. CREDIT: D Padgett (IPAC/Caltech), W Brandner (IPAC), K Stapelfeldt (JPL) and NASA
35. Disks in the infrared. CREDIT: C Burrows (STScI), the WF/PC-2 Science Team and NASA
36. Another planet? CREDIT: S Terebey (Extrasolar Research Corp.) and NASA
37. The Hubble Deep Field. CREDIT: K Ratnatunga, R Griffiths (Carnegie Mellon University) and NASA
38. Barred spiral galaxy NGC 4639. CREDIT: A Sandage (Carnegie Observatories), A Saha (STScI), G A Tammann, L Labhardt (Astronomical Institute, University of Basel), F D Macchetto and N Panagia (STScI/ESA) and NASA
39. Cepheids in the galaxy NGC 1365. CREDIT: W Freedman (Carnegie Observatories), the HST Key Project Team and NASA
40. Spiral galaxy NGC 4314. CREDIT: G F Benedict, A Howell, J Jorgensen, D Chapell (University of Texas), J Kenney (Yale University), B J Smith (CASA, University of Colorado) and NASA

INDEX

Page numbers in italic refer to illustrations of specific objects. Terms which have their own entry in the Glossary are not indexed.